F
Find..., ...

"*Finding Lifelines* is a novel that will help any teacher navigate their first year of teaching and beyond. Using scenarios and practical advice, Grieve and Sharos did an amazing job creating a story that will resonate with educators, no matter how long they have been in the profession. This book inspires me to provide the necessary support to all teachers, helping them find success and happiness in the profession."

—**Ryan Sheehy**, educator, learner, author, speaker

"This book is full of wisdom. It will inspire teachers and make them feel less alone, but Sharos and Grieve's underlying message—of empathy, preparation, hard work, and humility—will also apply to any profession. I found it moving, wise, hopeful, and, if I were a young teacher, helpful. I genuinely enjoyed the narrative, but the eye needs a place to rest. The Post-it notes and journal entries provide little oases along the way."

—**Steve Rushin**, *Sports Illustrated* journalist, award-winning novelist

"*Finding Lifelines* is an extraordinary professional learning book. The engaging fictional story sets a backdrop for many valuable and important lessons for all educators, including new teachers, veteran teachers, and administrators. I found myself immersed in the story and nodding along every step of the way. Grieve and Sharos have created a wonderful, uplifting, and real book that is a joy to read."

—**Allyson Apsey**, elementary principal, author of *Through the Lens of Serendipity*

"*Finding Lifelines* is a beautifully penned story that shares the real life of educators today. It is a tale we can all relate to, and the lessons revealed through the characters are invaluable and timeless.

"From the novice teacher navigating her way through the first year of this wonderful profession to the seasoned educator stretching herself to reach new levels of personal growth, the story feels real. I appreciate how the authors interwove lessons throughout each chapter to create natural discussion topics of conversation and self-searching. Prepare to be inspired and motivated to do and teach better because of this book."

—Tara Martin, educator, speaker, author of
Be REAL and *Cannonball In*

"Grieve and Sharos share an engaging and true-to-life story of first-year teacher Jill Cordera. An endearing narrative, the book uses Jill's personal reflections with others' viewpoints, including veteran teacher Tiana Williams and Vice Principal Brian Pribaz, to illustrate what makes schools transformative, students special, teaching rewarding, and our profession unique. The story was right-sized with relevant takeaways. I found myself at times smiling and at other times emotionally reminiscent. I thought back to my own first year of teaching, felt like I was actually there, and learned something new all over again. Well done!"

—Dr. Ryan Donlan, author, consultant,
university professor

"You will identify with at least one character in *Finding Lifelines* by Grieve and Sharos! Depending on your educational experience, you may identify with each of them. This novel has implications and lessons for educators of today, tomorrow, and always. Not only did I feel rejuvenated as I recalled my first days in the classroom but I also felt excited and empowered by what is to come. You'll want to read *Finding Lifelines* again and again!"

—Alicia Ray, educator, speaker, author of
Educational Eye Exam

"Teaching is the most honorable profession. It's hard, and there are emotional ups and downs. In *Finding Lifelines*, Grieve and Sharos deliver a powerful reminder that peer support will allow all teachers to thrive and flourish as they prepare our youth for their future. With the support and wisdom of veteran teachers, our faith is restored that teachers can and should face the difficulties and seek the lifelines in one of the greatest and most noble professions."

—Michael Lubelfeld, author, superintendent

"This is an incredible read for new and veteran teachers alike. There is a strong emphasis on the power of building and maintaining relationships throughout. As an educator, I appreciate the authentic depictions of the struggles and successes of students, teachers, and administrators."

—**Todd Harris**, assistant principal

"*Finding Lifelines* is the captivating story of a new teacher in her first professional year. The authors cleverly use the book's central characters to offer advice to educators. Instead of writing another how-to book, Grieve and Sharos invite the reader to learn from the protagonist's favorite college professor, who shares his wisdom through a series of Post-it notes (also meant to be used by the reader). We also meet an experienced teacher who befriends our heroine during her first rocky week and offers wisdom at every stage of her year. What a wonderful way to help guide young teachers! It's engaging, and it works."

—**Dr. Kristen Foster**, professor, Marquette University

FINDING LIFELINES

A Practical Tale About *Teachers* and *Mentors*

Andrew Grieve   *Andrew Sharos*

Finding Lifelines
© 2019 by Andrew Grieve and Andrew Sharos

This book is available at special discounts when purchased in quantity for use as premiums, promotions, fundraisers, or for educational use. For inquiries and details, contact the publisher at books@daveburgessconsulting.com.

Published by Dave Burgess Consulting, Inc.
San Diego, CA
DaveBurgessConsulting.com

Cover Design by Genesis Kohler
Editing and Interior Design by My Writers' Connection

Library of Congress Control Number: 2019949110
Paperback ISBN: 978-1-949595-76-5
Ebook ISBN: 978-1-949595-77-2

First Printing: September 2019

CONTENTS

FOREWORD

The most important asset of a school is its teachers; they represent the most critical factor in raising student learning and achievement. Teachers are the human capital of a school, and the more we invest in our teacher capital, the more they will improve their useful outputs over long periods of time. In *Finding Lifelines*, the characters struggle to discover how to improve their ability to change students' lives as they balance the pressures of teaching, interacting with students and fellow faculty members, and achieving a work/life balance.

If a teacher is struggling to learn the basics of how to run a classroom, that teacher needs a tutor. If a teacher's classroom and instruction are moving well, but they aren't getting the very best out of the students, that teacher needs a coach. If a teacher is inspired, we can be certain that this person has a mentor. In *Finding Lifelines*, the authors seek to portray the evolution of these three roles within the context of a young teacher's first year of teaching. Not only that, but they describe a wonderfully reciprocal relationship between a young teacher who seeks to improve her craft and an older teacher seeking to keep up with the changing world around her. The third major character, an administrator, seeks to provide school leadership while balancing the demands of his new role.

There are many ways to excite, influence, and motivate students, and one of the best techniques is the use of a discrepant event. A discrepant event is something that doesn't make sense to the mind, even while we stare at it in disbelief. This seed of doubt is enough to pique any student's curiosity. In the book you hold in your hands, the main character, Jill, employs a discrepant event that would be possible only with the use of technology; she has her students collaborate and construct meaning with students thousands of miles away. But this event serves two different functions in the story: It is the catalyst for an older colleague to investigate her own professional growth and an important point in the development of the new teacher. We should highlight these lessons and celebrate those "light bulb" moments for teachers like we do with our students.

It is within the context of a young educator learning the art of teaching that this book highlights the difficulties and triumphs in our profession. The story is one that will be familiar and interesting to anyone who seeks to learn to teach, is currently learning to teach, or for the teacher who simply wants to get better. The book intersperses lively scenes and compelling characters in a convincing narrative that will strike the reader as authentic and engaging. To be an effective teacher, you must make a conscious decision to be positive and to set high expectations—for both your students and yourself. This story's main characters thrive on positivity and set high expectations, and it is the dramatic presentation of these ideas that gives the book life. In an engaging style, *Finding Lifelines* helps the reader imagine the difficult path of being and staying positive, not only to help ourselves but to help others in the service of a noble cause.

Each day the most important gift we can give our students is to be consistent. Many of our students come from homes where chaos and unpredictability may be the norm. In this book, we see the students who have stressful lives come alive in the realistic classroom that could very well be yours. The creation of this classroom is portrayed with plenty of challenges and obstacles rather than as an easy series of events. It will strike the reader as faithful to the process of creating a meaningful experience for students, a classroom which nurtures their achievement.

Finally, the journal entries and notes dispersed throughout the novel feel real and tangible. It is in this context that the authors deliver the impactful advice passed down from one generation of teachers to the next. One thing is true about this book—it is honest.

Enjoy the story, find the inspiration, and heed the practical advice.

Dr. Harry K. Wong
author of *The First Days of School*

—— 1 ——

Jill stood on the campus of Marquette University looking at Professor Strus. He was bent with age, bald, and wearing large bifocal glasses that dominated his face. As always, he wore a plaid button-down shirt and baggy khaki trousers. Jill had enrolled in three of his classes in the education department. More than anyone else, he had formed her ideas on teaching. Strus had asked her to stop to meet him that afternoon before she left campus after graduation. Graduation had come and gone in a wave of long talks with friends, congratulatory meals with family, half-hearted parties, and forlorn goodbyes. Now, Jill was about to get in her little blue hatchback and drive off to a new life and a new teaching job.

As she listened to Strus talk about their time at Marquette together, she thought about how much she would miss him, his tutelage, his friendship, and most of all, his wise words. Abruptly, he stopped speaking and looked at Jill.

"Jill, you're one of my favorite students of all time," he said, "and you have all the makings of an incredible teacher. You're kind and thoughtful. You know your content, and you're not full of . . . you know. You're honest. But understand this is a profession that will test your toughness every day. We've talked about your self-confidence before. You can't allow other people to knock you off center."

Professor Strus paused and peered at Jill. For a moment, Jill wondered what would come next.

"I am going to be honest with you. I'm sad to see you go, and I want to help you get started. I would like to email you every week on a Monday morning. No, let's say Sunday night. Actually, I'll email you whenever I have a thought I think will apply to you. The contents of my email," he said, "should be written, by you, on a sticky note and placed on your refrigerator. What do you think?"

"I will absolutely do that, Professor Strus," Jill said. "I really appreciate it. I am sure it is going to be an interesting year. Maybe teaching is going to be difficult, and if it is, I'll be glad to have you in my corner."

Professor Strus nodded. "You're a good egg, Jill. Don't forget to read the email. I'll send you some things to think about." With that, he smiled, raised his hand in an awkward wave, and turned to walk down the sidewalk toward Schroeder Hall.

2

F our months later, on the first day of school, Jill bounded up
the stairs to the second floor of Silverado School. She walked
quickly down the deserted hallway smelling the scent of freshly
waxed floors, but when she came into sight of the courtyard, she
stopped and looked around her.

I'm a teacher, she thought. *I'm finally going to do it.*

She had been in the third grade the first time she told her
father she wanted to be a teacher. It was just after a parent-teacher
conference where the teacher had complimented her hard work.
She had walked quietly alongside her father back to the car that
evening. Then, just as they had reached the car, Jill said, in a voice
barely above a whisper, "I want to be a teacher."

Her father had nodded to her and said, "I think you'd be a
good one." Then he had gazed down at her with pride, and she
had seen it. Jill had known in that moment that she would become
a teacher.

Now, looking down the hallway with its gleaming floors, Jill
knew she had been right all along. She was fortunate to start her

teaching career at a school just a few miles from where she had grown up. She took comfort in knowing the neighborhood and even a little about the kids she would be teaching.

Jill took a deep breath. A sense of drama, of what would happen in the next few hours, filled the air. She walked to her room and stood in front of the door.

This is my room, she thought. She got out the new keys the friendly woman in the front office had given her two weeks ago and opened the door to her classroom, turned on the lights, and looked at the desks. Thirty desks in evenly spaced rows shone in front of her.

Forty-five minutes later, Jill sat looking at the student desks that would soon fill, her pulse racing. Panic and doubt ran through her mind. *How am I going to do this—teach these kids?* She took a deep breath and reminded herself of all the preparation she had done.

Now, it was fourteen minutes until class began. She looked at her lesson plans, written out in small, neat letters in her new book with its dark green cover. Last night, sitting on her couch, the plan had seemed great. She would start the class with a brief introduction, hand out a survey, and then lead a question-and-answer session.

What could go wrong?

She stood up. Then she sat down again. It was too soon to go out and wait for the students to arrive. She picked up a pencil and wondered if she should make some sort of note or something. She looked at the pile of copies on her desk. She looked at her laptop screen, but her e-mail inbox was empty.

Suddenly, she wondered if she had made enough copies of the survey. Maybe she had walked out of the duplicating center before the machine was done! Hands shaking, she started to count the

> It is always acceptable to be intrigued and nervous about a new situation. It means you care enough about what is about to happen.

copies. Just then, the door to her classroom opened and Tiana, a veteran teacher, walked quickly into the room.

"Happy opening day! Everything okay?" Tiana asked.

"Yes. Sure. Everything is fine," Jill said, her mouth twitching as she tried to smile convincingly.

Tiana leaned forward and pointed a long finger at her.

"Day one. Are you nervous?" Tiana asked quietly. Without waiting for a response from Jill, Tiana continued. "Don't worry. Just do your best. That's all anyone can ask of you. If you have any problems, I'm right next door. Except third period. Then I'm in another hallway somewhere. I don't know where."

Jill laughed.

"You don't know where your third period class is?" she asked.

Tiana shook her head.

"Nope. But it's not third period yet," she said. "Remember, I'm here if you want to talk about lesson planning any time." She smiled at Jill. "Let me know if you need anything. And listen— you're going to be great."

Jill nodded.

Tiana left, closing the door behind her. Jill's spirits rose for a minute. She had someone she could genuinely count on.

Then Jill had another thought. *Tiana was one person she absolutely could not disappoint.*

Tiana had predicted that Jill would be a good teacher, and to turn out to be something else was unthinkable.

A barely perceptible rapping sound interrupted her anxious thoughts.

Jill squinted at the door. It was coming from outside the classroom. Jill checked the time. There were ten minutes left before the students were supposed to arrive. Jill got up and walked hesitantly toward the door.

Sometimes we remember the first day of school. But almost always, we remember the first impression.

She looked through the safety glass into the hallway. Outside, a small girl looked up at her. Jill opened the door.

"Ms. Cordera?" the girl asked.

For some reason, "Ms. Cordera," coming from this little girl, startled Jill.

"Yes," Jill replied to the student. "Is this your first class?"

Jill's voice sounded strange to her, and the little girl looked at her quizzically.

"Is this your first year?" the girl asked.

Jill's mouth twitched, and she made a noise that sounded like a combination of yes, no, and maybe.

The girl nodded and then said quietly, "I won't tell the other kids." She paused for a moment, as if she were considering something, seemed to decide against it, and then said, "Can I come in?"

3

Tiana sat down at her desk and looked out the window at the morning sunlight flooding in through the partially closed blinds. She considered taking out her laptop and printing out a syllabus then shook her head, almost imperceptibly. Kids hated to be handed a syllabus on the first day. As she waited for the students to arrive, her mind suddenly went blank, and she had the strange feeling that she couldn't remember how to teach. She had been an educator for more than thirty years, but for a brief moment she wondered how in the world she was going to teach a room full of students.

Without thinking, she pulled the middle drawer of her desk open and took out a thick folder filled with thank you notes, handwritten letters, cards, and a few certificates.

One of the certificates said, "Teacher of the Year, Region IX."

She put it back in the folder and took out a card. "Mrs. Williams, you and I both know that I never would have made it without you. You saved me, and I will owe you forever. Stay cool and keep in touch. I will miss your class."

Tiana closed the folder and put it back in the middle drawer.

She closed her eyes. *Why did I look in that drawer?* she wondered. *I only look in there when I really need it . . .*

She scanned her memory for words to describe the moment. Nothing from Marcus Aurelius or Aristotle seemed appropriate. In her mind, she went through the *Nicomachean Ethics*, but none of it seemed suitable. She couldn't come up with a quotation that fit this particular situation, but then a thought of her own bubbled to the surface: *The teacher is lost who thinks that he or she has the answer to every question. The great teacher must be the perpetual student.*

That's good, she thought. *I need to write that down.*

An idea came to her, slowly at first, but then appearing fully formed. She was near her retirement, but she still had time to mentor a few more young teachers. Throughout her career, Tiana had worked with several young teachers and had loved watching them grow. Seeing Jill before first period, so nervous to start teaching, reminded her how it was to start teaching. *This year,* she thought, *I will keep a journal for Jill and fill it with advice and encouragement. It will be my gift to her at the end of the year.* She pulled a blank notebook from a desk drawer, opened it, and wrote the title on the first page: *Finding Lifelines.*

4

"No man steps in the same river twice, for it's not the same river, and he is not the same man."

The sign hung boldly on the wall of Vice Principal Pribaz's office. Brian sat at his desk in the administrative wing of the school. He looked around the office then at his name badge placed carefully on the bulletin board. BRIAN PRIBAZ, VICE PRINCIPAL.

His title *Vice Principal* still felt strange to him. He was proud to have earned the promotion, but in doing so, he felt as if he'd left his friends behind. An hour earlier, he had said hello to a teacher in the parking lot, a man he'd worked with for six years.

The teacher seemed to hesitate before offering his own greeting. "You're one of them," the hesitation had seemed to say. "You're not a teacher anymore."

Brian knew he wasn't the same man who had walked into the building six years ago. He had struggled at first. He'd worked hard to become a good teacher, and after a few years, he finally felt comfortable in the classroom. He sometimes felt he had peaked at the right time because the job of vice principal had come up, and he was qualified. At least on paper.

He had no idea what those qualifications meant when it came to doing this particular job, however. The methods and skills required to be a good teacher were very different from those necessary to be an administrator.

When he had interviewed for his job as a teacher, there were nine hundred applicants for his job. How he had survived the interview process alone was still a mystery to him. After the first round of interviews, he remembered feeling that he had a foot in the door, which meant there was one still outside the door.

But he had made it in—with both feet—and found his stride as a teacher. Not that there hadn't been a few missteps along the way, like the time the Assistant Superintendent had made an unannounced appearance in his classroom. He had listened as Brian droned on about the differences between the federalists and the anti-federalists in the early American republic. Thankfully, the room was dark enough that the Assistant Superintendent couldn't actually see the students' eyes rolling to the backs of their heads as the PowerPoint slides advanced mechanically. That terrifying day, Brian made a silent vow to do something better in his classes, but the scene had replayed itself in yesterday morning's faculty meeting.

"I, uh, realize that I'm the only thing standing between you and lunch," Brian said just before starting a PowerPoint presentation that he'd been forced to give about the increase in disciplinary referrals over the last year.

The teachers chuckled politely and then dutifully watched the presentation as Brian rambled on until the final slide. "Are there any questions?" Brian asked.

He had hoped that the promise of lunch would have been enough to make the faculty silent. Then one of the older faculty members stood up and asked a question about the tardy policy. It had, technically, been a question, but the tone was confrontational.

"What is the administration doing about getting students to class on time? Absences and tardies go hand in hand, especially at the beginning of the school day."

A number of responses had flashed through Brian's mind. The silence of the auditorium seemed to pressure him for a brilliant idea, but he hadn't wanted to offer any of them before checking with the principal, Mike Pasztor. Brian stood in front of the entire faculty and said, "I will look into this problem, and I will get back to you."

That was all he had to offer.

Time had seemed to stop. Brian asked if there were any more questions because he knew that it was a conversation ender then said something vague about where the staff was serving lunch.

One faculty member peered at him while saying to another teacher, "No one wants lunch to be here more than this guy . . ."

Brian shook his head at the memory then took out his phone and checked the time. He looked out the window at the students walking into the building. The kids were laughing, shouting, carrying new backpacks, and it seemed like a beautiful, dramatic show—one filled with thousands of actors filing onto a big stage where a great deal of their lives would take place during the next nine months. Brian was suddenly painfully aware of the role he had to play in this overarching drama, but he took a deep breath and welcomed it.

5

Jill stood outside of Taft's Bar for a moment, looking at the traffic going past on North Avenue and thinking about her first day as a teacher. She hadn't had time to think all day as streams of students walked in and out of her room. She was amazed at the energy of the students. She stood in front of students, making decision after decision, answering question after question.

"Can I go to the bathroom?"

"No."

"Are we supposed to write this down?"

"Yes."

"Do you have a boyfriend?"

"No."

"Do you have any pets?"

"No."

"Are we going to have homework in this class?"

"Yes."

Was she winning? Was she losing? She realized in a moment that there was little time for reflection while teaching.

She had dreamt of changing lives, of being the kind of teacher filmmakers made movies about.

Was this how it started?

She didn't even know where to go to get a stapler.

Jill remembered how she stood outside her first period class, holding a stack of freshly copied surveys, which were slowly getting soaked by the perspiration coming from her hands.

Tiana stood next door, greeting students.

"We missed you over the summer, Mrs. Williams!"

"We love you, Mrs. Williams!"

"My brother has you this year, Mrs. Williams!"

The sheer number of students who went up to Tiana at the beginning of the day overwhelmed Jill. *Was that what being a teacher was like? A constant stream of admirers?*

Comparison to others can be a thief of joy.

Jill tried to greet every student who entered the room, but she had noticed that her mouth had become dry in the process.

Then the bell rang—the beginning of the period. It would be forty-eight minutes before she could stop. She walked into the classroom, shut the door behind her, and in a nervous voice said, "Good morning. I'm Ms. Cordera. Welcome to class, everybody."

The students stared at her in absolute silence. She could feel them hanging on her every word as they formed their first impressions of her.

It was there in the awkward silence that Jill noticed how long the room was and how much space there was between the rows. To Jill, the room had seemed gigantic, with the students growing larger and larger by the second—until it seemed the students in the front row were towering over her. Exactly at that point, Jill blinked, and everything returned to normal, except that she could feel her heart beating hard in her chest.

"I'm going to hand out a syllabus and go over some of the rules and procedures of the classroom," she said.

Just then, a boy in the back of the class coughed and said something at the same time. The group of boys around him laughed.

Jill continued, "I'm looking forward to a great year." The nervous twitch that began under her right eye made that comment hard, if not impossible, to believe.

It wasn't until she started reading through the syllabus that she realized how boring it would be.

Really boring.

To her, to the kids, to anyone watching from the hallway.

As she read the rules of the classroom, the students began a quiet, open rebellion. Students had quiet conversations with one another, ignoring her, and Jill had raised her voice a bit. The students then raised their voices in response, and the result was she needed to stop them before they got to Rule #6, "Raise your hand and be recognized before speaking."

Suddenly, the door opened, and Vice Principal Pribaz walked in and sat down at her desk.

He was a tall, serious-looking man, and not quite as old as Jill had imagined a vice principal would be. Pribaz checked his phone habitually, and she noticed that he carried two of them.

Jill wondered if there was anything incriminating on her desk, like a sticky note that said something like, "Remember to figure out how to teach before seventh period."

She couldn't remember what was on her desk.

Jill's thoughts rushed through her mind as she tried to appear calm at the front of the room.

What is he doing in the room?

Had the class been making too much noise?

Can he see me sweating?

Is he going to fire me right here on the spot?

Find your center and focus on your why. These actions will drive you toward success in the difficult moments.

His presence had made the class quiet, but Jill became so nervous she felt like she was having an out-of-body experience. Her voice—harsh, grating, barely in control—hadn't seemed like hers, and she noticed her hands shaking slightly as she handed out a questionnaire for the students to fill out.

Can he see my hands shaking?

To her surprise, the students focused on the questionnaire.

Is that all it takes to get them to be quiet? Jill wondered.

At that point, Pribaz nodded at her in a satisfied way, stood up, and walked out.

Maybe I just passed the first test, Jill thought.

Finally, the bell rang and the students rushed out of the room. Jill was absolutely certain that most of them had not heard her say that the questionnaire was homework.

But at that moment, she didn't care. She stood there, in silence, at the front of the room, looking at the empty desks.

She had done it. She had made it through first period.

A bit of a commotion at the door brought her back to the present as the classroom began to fill once again.

That's right! I have to teach five more classes!

Kids would continue to stream in until she taught all of them.

How do teachers do this? she thought. And then another thought crossed her mind. *Why do they do it?*

After the students were seated, Jill greeted her second period class with what she hoped was a cheerful, "Good morning!"

But even to her ears, her greeting sounded forced and strange.

The students looked at her, then one another, silently.

Fighting to control her own boredom as she went through the syllabus, she moved quickly through some of the details and got to the questionnaire faster. This seemed to work better, but she noticed that, whereas her first period had been sleepy and lacking in energy, her second period class was wide awake. Instead of speaking to one another in muted mumbling, second period had talked more in conversational tones.

Another unusual thing was how they spoke to one another as if Jill wasn't in the room.

A teacher's confidence comes from an awareness of his or her strengths.

One girl, Camilla, turned to her friend and said, "Is she a substitute, or are we going to have her all year?"

Jill had interrupted and suggested she would be there until June.

Camilla's eyes had met hers with a look that was equal measures of defiance and fury.

"So you're going to learn to teach with us? This class is going to suck," Camilla added after a pause. But she just shrugged and continued to fill out her questionnaire.

"I don't think that is an appropriate way to speak," Jill commented.

Camilla looked back at Jill and then said, "Can I go to the bathroom?"

"Take the pass," Jill muttered.

By the end of the period, Jill had been forced to yell over the class. She forgot to take attendance in her next class and received a reminder email from the attendance lady.

And all of that had been before lunch.

To make matters worse, she'd failed to make enough copies for her sixth period class, and this had left her so shaken that, by the time her seventh period class showed up, Jill had decided to scrap the syllabus and talk to the students about how their first day had been. The students had seemed to welcome this, and it gave Jill a moment to relax in an otherwise exhausting day.

At the end of the period, Jill stood in the middle of the classroom, surrounded by empty student desks. She thought she heard the bell ring a few minutes earlier and dismissed her class. It wasn't until she noticed that her class was the only one in the hallway that she realized that the bell hadn't rung.

When the bell actually did ring, Jill sank into one of the student desks, drained of energy.

Do I really have to do this tomorrow? And the next day? she thought. That's when Tiana appeared in her classroom, looking almost comically calm.

"Jill, how about talking over a beer at Taft's? We should celebrate the completion of your first day. The beer is on me."

Jill said yes immediately, while thinking that her time might be better spent planning for the next day. And the week after that.

Tiana's Journal

There is nothing more important to me than helping a young teacher. I want you to feel like you are supported and cared for. It can be so tough to start out in this profession, and today I tried to help by making sure you feel that you have someone to listen to you and give you advice if you ask for it.

It was wonderful to see the attention you so obviously pay to this noble profession. Every teacher possesses strengths that might make him or her a great teacher. The trick is to find out what those strengths are and capitalize on them.

There is so much to learn when you start teaching, and yet if I present everything I know about teaching all at once, I will overwhelm you. So I'm writing in this journal instead. I know this isn't going to help you now, but I will honestly try to unfold some of this advice at a compassionate pace. If you aren't ready to hear it in the moment, I will have the satisfaction of knowing that the advice is here, in this journal, whenever you need it. That may prove a cold comfort to me, and only you will ever be able to tell me if I have done my best.

The first day of school can be rough. Even veteran teachers will tell you that. Most of us don't sleep well the night before, regardless of how long we've been teaching. Even our bodies take a while to respond to the hours on our feet interacting with kids.

It is so very difficult to be kind to yourself as you take time to reflect. But please do that. In order to help you do that, let me pose some questions.

Why did you choose teaching as a profession?

Can you remember the day you declared education as your major?

Do you remember how hard it was to study for finals and write papers in college?

Remember how thrilling it was to see that first kid smile during your student teaching?

Remember that first compliment you received from a student?

Use all of these moments and all of these choices to drive you forward as you begin to teach. Keep them close to you when you fail. Your special answers to these questions are at the center of what makes you an individual, and they can make you a great teacher.

Return to the moments in your life that made you want to become a teacher. How you feel about this first day is a direct reflection of what you focus on. That all depends on where you aim the lens. You can focus on the positive or negative aspects. It is your choice.

Focus on your center. What makes you who you are as a teacher? What kind of teacher do you want to become? What drives you when you get up in the morning? What is your why — your personal and special why?

Write down your why, and put it where you can see it at night and in the morning. Make sure you see it every day and never forget why you are a teacher. Focus on the why and you will find your center.

6

So Jill had driven to Taft's at the end of the day and stood looking at the traffic move past, thinking about her first day. As she walked into Taft's, she spotted Tiana sitting in a booth near the back. Giving a quick wave, she made her way to her colleague and collapsed into the booth, clearly exhausted and defeated. Tiana waited, pausing to give Jill time to collect herself.

"So—how was the first day?" Tiana asked.

"Um, somewhere between horrible and embarrassing," Jill responded.

"That bad?"

"Actually worse. This is me being positive," Jill said, not even attempting a smile.

"I can still remember my first day of teaching," Tiana said.

"How long ago was that?"

Tiana moved her head to the side, looked at Jill, and said, "Thirty years."

"How have you done it?" Jill asked. Rather than wait for a response, her words came out in a flood. "I was at school for eight hours, and I'm ready for winter break. How do you do it? How does anyone do it? I'm hoping for a snow day, and it's August. The kids didn't like me. I can barely get their attention, and when I do, they look like they're about to fall asleep. I talked on and on about nothing. *I* hated listening to me today. Some of them even said some stuff under their breath that I pretended I couldn't hear. But the horrible thing is, they might be *right*.

Tiana looked at her closely. "Jill, teaching is hard," she said gently. "It's really hard to get the kids' attention. It's hard to keep it, but there *are* some things that can make your life a lot easier."

"But I see kids in your class," Jill said. "They look like they're having a good time! They look like they actually *like* you. The things they say to you when they walk in . . ."

Tiana nodded slowly. "Yeah, well, you didn't see me in my first year, or my second, or my third. It takes a lot of time to work through all of the things that make kids love a class. Once you work through those things, the kids will do the rest."

"But it looks so natural when you're up there in front of them," Jill protested.

If you err on the side of your students, you can rarely go wrong.

"It's not natural. It's all been practiced. Every joke, every movement. I can tell you that almost no one is a natural teacher."

The bartender came out from behind the bar and walked up to their booth.

"Jill, this is Big Mike. What'll you have?"

Jill ordered a beer, thanked Big Mike, and turned back to Tiana.

"So how do I become like you?" she said.

"Well, the first thing is that you're being much too hard on yourself," Tiana said. "If you just *survive* your first year, you're doing well. Now, having said that, we always have to push ourselves. This is the only time you will ever teach these particular kids. This is your one chance with them. So the quicker you get your stuff together, the better."

"How do I make the kids sit down and actually do work?" Jill asked.

"Procedure," Tiana said immediately. "The kids have to walk in and know what to expect. You need a bell ringer, then move right into your first set. Read Harry Wong's *The First Days of School*."

"You don't do that!" Jill said, shocked by the shrillness of her voice. "I'm sorry, I didn't mean to yell at you; it's just that I've seen you at the beginning of class. You're standing there drinking coffee, joking with the students."

"Sure, that's what I do now," Tiana said. "But a young teacher needs to get the students trained in doing the right thing at the beginning of class. Every class needs to learn where the line is. Once they find the line, you can move it and let them have more fun, but you have to draw a line first."

Jill and Tiana stopped talking for moment, and Big Mike walked up with Jill's beer. Jill looked across the room. She was suddenly struck by the idea that this was a nice place to come for a drink, and that if she could meet with Tiana on a regular basis and get some advice, maybe she would be okay. She narrowed her eyes a bit and let that thought sink in.

It might actually be okay.

"You're young," Tiana said. "This job will change you. Nothing matures a person faster and more deeply than the sustained responsibility for another person's welfare."

Tiana paused for a moment and then said, almost to herself, "Nothing makes you older than responsibility."

> Some teachers will be judged solely on how they treat their kids. Ethically, it's the most important part of the job, but practically, it's the core of what we do.

At that moment, Jill looked up at a man standing in front of the booth. It took a moment before she recognized him as the young vice principal who had visited her first period class. Her mouth dropped open a little.

Is he going to think I go out for beers every night? Jill thought.

"Hey, Brian," Tiana said. "Have a seat."

"Thanks," Brian nodded and then looked at Jill.

"I don't usually drink this early in the day," Jill said defensively.

"I do," Brian said, and Jill laughed.

"I figured the two of you might want a drink after starting your new jobs today," Tiana said. "Was the first day as long for you as it was for me?"

Jill looked back and forth between Brian and Tiana.

"How much time do you have?" Brian said.

"So, wait, you two are friends?" Jill asked.

"We talk all the time. We taught together for six years, and just because he's in administration now doesn't mean we can't hang out."

Jill looked at Brian. Against her instincts, she blurted out, "I can't make the kids do what I say. This girl Camilla openly disrespected me in class!"

Tiana and Brian nodded in silence.

"Camilla Gonzalez?" Brian asked. "I worked with her in a study program last year. She's got a hard shell, but down deep she's a good kid."

Jill bristled at his comment. *A good kid wouldn't have said what she said*, Jill thought.

Tiana sipped her beer and then turned to Jill. "We can take a look at this problem with your students in two ways," Tiana said. "The first way is the philosophical way. In teaching, we have to be masters of prediction. We have to see what a student's potential is, even if that student doesn't see it herself. Even if the parents don't see it, we have to sense what trajectory this student might be on in an ideal world. Then we have to make sure that the student knows what that trajectory might be and help them get on it."

Jill took in what Tiana said then responded, "That's great, and I really believe you, but today they had no interest in paying attention to me."

Brian looked across the bar, slowly moving his gaze from one end to the other. Finally, he shrugged and added, "Camilla is testing you. It's the first day, and she sees right through you. So be human. Let her know that you are on her team, and that you aren't there to give her a hard time. Students want to know that you are fighting for them, not against them. You can be firm. But the moment you write a referral or send a note to the dean, you are going to lose that relationship forever. Win the relationship; that's the goal. You want her to work and listen in class, right? The only way you are going to do that is by saving the relationship."

Some kids will test you. But the real test is how you respond.

"So how do I do that after what happened today?" Jill asked.

"You have to learn to be consistent with praise and punishment," Tiana said. "It's a really hard thing, and most people can't get the hang of it. You tell the student what is going to happen if they do this or that, and then without fail, you follow through with what you said you'd do."

"I get that, but what am I supposed to do with Camilla?" Jill asked.

"I'd speak to her after class, or before class if you can manage it, and make sure she knows you are going to try to make the class as good as it can be. *For her.* That you're in this to make sure that *she* gets the most out of school."

"But what if she doesn't change?" Jill asked.

"Yeah, well, at the end of your little talk, hold her to some kind of agreement, like she is not going to be disrespectful in your class, and if she does, there'll be consequences," Tiana said.

Jill nodded and took a sip of beer. It all sounded really simple sitting around after work, but it wouldn't be so simple in her classroom.

"Kids have this innate ability to figure out who cares about them and who doesn't. They can figure out whether you'll be the teacher who will discipline them or not," Tiana said.

"We'll support you," said Brian. "Just try some of the tools in your toolbox first."

The three of them sat in a comfortable silence for a moment, and then Tiana turned to Brian and asked him about his day. He spoke for a time about his fear that crossing the line into administration had changed people's perceptions of him. Listening to him, Jill was surprised at just how reflective he was, despite his polished exterior.

Tiana's Journal

We must believe in ourselves before we can expect anyone else to. At this point in your career, your belief in yourself can be based solely on your ability to try hard. When you walk into the classroom, the students should be thinking to themselves with certainty, "My teacher will help me get this done." They must have faith in you, and in this way you will be appealing to their hearts and not just their minds.

Students have to feel the strength of your care for them on the level of their emotions, their motivations, and their burdens when they enter your classroom. When you understand these motivations, emotions, and obstacles and help them succeed, you can begin to believe that their success is possible. Your kids desperately need to know that you believe in them, so they can begin to believe in themselves.

Your first day was a tough day. But storms make roots grow stronger. I saw a willingness in you to listen and to learn, which are two tremendous assets to have in this profession. I am glad that you were comfortable talking about your difficulties so openly. Strategically seek out people to listen and help.

Be friendly with your students, but not friends. Establish boundaries and, like Brian is always saying, "Win the relationship." Be confident in what you are doing and allow students to wrestle with the content enough to fail. Pick them up and encourage them. Through failure and through work, you and the students will both gain confidence.

This was only the first day of school, and tomorrow you can erase some of this. Be patient with yourself, always.

7

It wasn't long before Jill noticed that the school operated almost like a small village. It had its own language, its own habits, and its own important people. Tiana had told Jill that it was critical for her to be out in the hallway during passing period, and on her way to the cafeteria, Jill noticed the interaction between teachers and students in the halls.

Jill went through the lunch line, and nothing else made her feel like an outsider as much as when the older teachers and the cafeteria ladies spoke to each other with obvious familiarity. One of the maintenance men walked through and called over to a short, gray-haired man sitting across the room.

"Hello, Mr. Watson," he said.

"Hey, Bobby," the older man called back.

"Back in room three sixteen again this year?"

How many years do you have to work some place before you know the room numbers and who teaches in them? Jill wondered as she walked through the cafeteria and surveyed the groups of teachers.

At one table was a group of gray-haired men, some wearing sweat-shirts bearing a likeness of Silverado's mascot, the Jackrabbit.

Shrill laughter rose from a group at another table. One woman was on her phone rather than eating lunch. The explosive sound of their laughter gave Jill pause, and she turned to a table filled with younger-looking teachers. A few of the teachers nodded to her as she sat down, but no one took any particular interest in her.

"Do what they see," a young teacher in rectangular black glasses and a turtleneck was saying.

"Filling out that athletic eligibility report is a big deal," a woman with blonde frizzy hair returned.

"Administration just cares about building their own resumes. So they start initiatives that they can talk about at conferences," Black Glasses said. "They have us all doing inquiry-based learning so they can go speak about creating innovative classrooms. We're the ones doing all the work."

"The kids can do some of the same stuff with a pencil and a piece of paper," the young woman replied. "But don't do that. If you get observed, they want to know that you're using technology."

Jill wondered what the words "athletic eligibility" meant, and within minutes of sitting down she questioned her seating choice. She started to get nervous that an administrator would walk in.

"I can't wait until I get tenure," the young woman continued. "Then I can stop coaching volleyball."

Jill's lunch had been like that, and at a certain point, between the embarrassment of being at this table and the curiosity and suspicion that these young teachers were giving her a view into the inner workings of the school, Jill wondered if she should just bring her lunch from home and eat in her classroom. She only had twenty minutes to eat anyway.

> Playing politics in the faculty's social scene is important but never at the expense of your values and beliefs.

Jill made a quick stop at the restroom and her mailbox before rushing back to her classroom. When the fifth-period bell rang, Jill passed out an outline that the students would complete based on their reading.

"Does she really expect us to do this crap?" a boy with tinted glasses said to no one in particular.

Jill stepped forward, and although she sensed her heartbeat thudding in her chest, she said, in what she hoped was a firm but pleasant tone, "The only thing that I want is for you to be successful when you get to the next class. When I was in school, I needed to learn how to take notes like this, and I wish someone had taught me."

Jill saw her reflection in the boy's tinted glasses, and there was a moment of silence between them before the boy turned back to his worksheet.

"Fair enough," the boy said in a noncommittal way.

Jill took a deep breath. She walked up and down the aisles, watching the students work. She looked out at the desks and realized that, for the first time in any of her classes, all of the students seemed to be on task. Some tension left her body, and she walked to the front of the room and turned around.

"Are we getting graded on this?" a girl asked.

Jill looked at the tiny girl who had spoken. The girl tapped her desk with an oversized pencil.

"Of course you're getting graded on this," Jill said sharply.

"Well, how much is it going to count for?"

Jill paused, unsure of what she should say. She had not given any thought to how many points an assignment like this should be worth. She realized that she should have had a ready answer, so she invented a point value.

"This assignment will be worth fifteen points," Jill said.

"Only fifteen points? Are you serious? I'm not doing this then," the little girl said.

A friendly-looking girl with straight-cut bangs looked up from her work. "What's worth fifteen points?" she asked.

"This assignment. It's only worth fifteen points," the little girl told her. "I'm not doing it."

"Well, you should want to do all of the assignments, shouldn't you?" Jill asked. "I mean, that's how you get better at the material, right?"

"Whatever. I don't think it's worth it," the little girl said.

The girl with the bangs put her pen down and glanced from Jill to her classmate.

A tall girl in the front row raised her hand. Jill looked at her.

"Yes, Alexis?" Jill said.

"Can I go to the bathroom?" Alexis asked.

"Yes," Jill said, turning back to the conversation. "What if I make it worth thirty points?"

"You're going to make it worth thirty points?" the girl with the bangs asked. "Just like that? Thirty points?"

Teachers often focus on the "what" they are teaching. Students often focus on the "who" is teaching them. Learning happens when we all focus on the "why."

"If it makes you focus, maybe it's worth more than I thought," Jill said.

The boy with the tinted glasses looked at her.

"Are you just making this all up as you go along?" the boy asked.

When he spoke, Jill's heart began to race, and her mouth became dry. She could feel perspiration break out along her hairline.

"How old are you, anyway?" he asked.

"I think that's a personal question," Jill said.

"She might be younger than you," the friendly girl with the bangs said to the boy in the tinted glasses.

"What college did you go to?" the little girl asked.

"I went to Marquette University," Jill answered.

"My brother goes there," the boy with the tinted glasses said. "When did you graduate?"

"Last year," Jill said after a pause.

"He probably knows you," the boy said.

"Maybe he does," Jill said, squinting with embarrassment. "Let's get back to work. The period is almost over, and what you don't finish is homework."

"But this is worth fifteen points right?" the little girl asked.

"I said thirty," Jill said.

"It's still not really worth doing if it's only thirty," the little girl said.

"I cannot force you to do it. The assignment is worth thirty points," Jill said.

"Why do I even bother?" the little girl yelled.

Jill was so surprised at this reaction that she took a step backward and bumped up against another student's desk.

"This class is a joke," the boy with the tinted glasses said calmly.

"This class is not a joke," Jill said. "You need it to graduate."

"I'll take it in summer school," the little girl said.

At that moment, the bell rang.

"What you didn't finish is homework!" Jill called out over the sound of students packing up and rushing out the door. She was sure that not one student would actually spend the time to finish the assignment. Her face was flushed, and a flash of anger spread through her as she moved out towards the hall, following the last of the students. A tall, thin boy with long, curly hair stood in the doorway.

"Don't listen to them, Ms. Cordera. You just try to teach us," he said in a quiet voice.

With that, he turned around and walked out into the hall.

8

Jill sat on the floor of her kitchen, with her back resting against a cabinet door. The cold linoleum felt good against the backs of her legs as she pressed her face into the palms of her hands. She felt that everything she had done to prepare to be a teacher had been a waste of time. She thought back to herself as a third-grader who dreamed of being a teacher.

Get a different dream, kid, Jill thought.

She hung her hands out in front of her and watched her fingers move slowly in the air. The words beneath her photo in her high school yearbook flashed in her memory: "Plans for the future include becoming a teacher."

Jill winced. That plan hadn't lasted very long in the real world. She thought of the other young teachers with whom she had eaten lunch that day. What if they found out the problems she was having? There would be no end to the gossip then.

Who loses a career this fast? she thought.

Jill slowly got to her feet and walked into the living room The stack of yesterday's student questionnaires sat neatly clipped

> There is no room
> in our minds
> for happiness if
> worry takes up
> all the space.

together on the coffee table. She looked at them but could not bear to sit down and read them. She walked around the living room then went into the kitchen to get a glass of water. She took a deep breath and returned to the living room. Sitting down on the couch, she reached for the stack and unclipped the questionnaires from her first-period class and began reading.

Underneath the question, "What responsibilities do you have outside of school?" one of the students, Madeline, had written, "I have to take care of my three younger sisters right after school." Jill read on. "My parents work until late at night. I love them very much. They work very hard."

The simplicity of Madeline's answer struck Jill. She could feel another emotion replacing the one that brought her close to tears. She couldn't find a name for it, but the emotion was something like calm curiosity.

She reread the last line. "They work very hard." Jill thought about that answer for a moment then began to feel guilty. These hard-working parents were sending their child to school assuming that Jill would teach her. But Jill could not even get their daughter to do a worksheet without listening to the other students arguing in class.

Jill wrote in small, precise lettering across the top of the assignment: "I would like to learn more about your parents. They sound like great people."

Jill read the rest of the girl's responses, and they all possessed a tone of quiet, simple devotion to family and the task at hand. Jill put the paper next to her on the couch and looked at the second questionnaire.

For two hours she sat there, in the half-light of her living room, reading the answers on the students' questionnaires. She tried to imagine their lives at home, tried to envision what they were doing at that very moment. She wondered if they were looking forward to the next day of school or whether they viewed it with the same fear that pressed in on her chest.

When Jill crawled into bed that night, the fear was still there. She thought about how she might make it go away, but all she could think of was the little girl in her class arguing about fifteen points.

Building relationships with students is like an Individual Education Plan. Each student requires a unique pathway and approach.

9

Jill walked into Tiana's classroom after school a few days later, put her bag on a student desk, and sat down, looking at Tiana.

"They're not doing homework," she said. "Whatever I do, whatever threats I have, however I express to them how important it is, they just do not do homework."

"Hi, Jill, how did your day go?" Tiana asked.

Jill laughed.

"I'm really sorry," Jill said. "My day has been fine. I'm just thinking about this homework problem thing."

"It's a battle," Tiana said. "It's a battle for us, the kids, and their parents. The thing to ask yourself is this: Is what you're giving out as homework really worth the battle? When my own kids had homework, it was painful, honestly. So is it worth it?"

"I think it is, yeah," Jill said. "I just do not have enough time in class to get through all of the things that we need to do. Our kids need to practice when they're not in front of me."

Tiana nodded.

"I get it," she said. "If we are asking the kids just to do enrichment at home, then I think we need to take another look at it. But if they are honestly doing things that are central to the class, and you really can't do it during the class period, then they have to do it at home."

"So how do you help kids to complete homework?" Jill asked.

"I know this woman who works as a personal trainer, and she told me a story about this other personal trainer she knows. He works in New York City, and he goes to rich people's houses and trains them one-on-one. He's trained celebrities, CEOs, all sorts of people. He charges a lot of money, and he's really good at what he does. He gets results."

Tiana looked at Jill and smiled.

"Don't worry," she said. "I'm getting to the point. So this personal trainer in New York City had a new client, and the only time that this guy had to work out was really early in the morning. So they set up the appointment, and this personal trainer guy shows up at this rich guy's penthouse, and the rich guy is ready to go, ready to work out, wearing his tracksuit, and it's like 5:00 a.m. The personal trainer says, 'Okay you're ready to go. You're up early. That's just great.' And the rich guy goes, 'So what are we going to do? Are we going to hit the weights? Am I going to run?' And this personal trainer guy turns to him and goes, 'No, you're just gonna sit down and read the paper. Right there in that chair. Just sit there.' And this rich guy's kind of angry, you know; he paid this guy to show up and train him. But the personal trainer said, 'The first step is for you to get used to waking up early, putting on your stuff, and getting ready to work out. Tomorrow, we'll go for a walk.'"

Jill frowned. "I mean, I'm not sure that I understand . . ." her voice trailed off.

"Just walk them into the idea of doing homework. Condition their minds to the concept of sitting down and doing something at home. Start off with something small. Like a vocabulary lesson, without a lot of words or anything. Just something they can do to get acclimated to the *idea* of doing homework."

Jill's face brightened.

> There is a lot more joy in learning than being taught. When we create conditions where students acquire knowledge on their own accord, we empower them.

"I get it. So can I just take that idea of doing some vocabulary work?"

"It's one of the great things about teaching," Tiana said. "You can steal anything from another teacher. Just give them credit. Why not have the kids at home use the vocab words in different contexts, writing using the words but something that they can do in five or ten minutes. Then when they get back to class, have them do a speed-dating-style thing with the vocabulary words. You know, like the outer circle rotates one person to their left. Something like that."

"I like that," Jill said. "And it's a good bell ringer."

Two days later, Jill's classroom was set up with a large outer ring and a smaller inner ring of desks.

"Okay, so what we're going to do is use the first vocabulary word in a sentence, and then your partner uses the second, and then you use the third if you're in the outer ring."

The students turned to their partners, and the room became alive with quick conversations using the vocabulary words Jill had assigned the night before. As they practiced, Jill walked around and checked off that the students had actually written two sentences for each word.

"And now, ladies and gentlemen, if you are in the inner ring, please move . . ." Jill leaned over and asked a quiet girl next to her for a number between one and five.

"Three," the girl whispered.

"If you are in the inner ring, please move three desks to your left," Jill said.

There was a scraping sound as feet shuffled around the inner ring. The students sat down, and Jill reminded them of the protocol, this time starting with the students in the inner ring.

All the students had done the homework, Jill noted. It had been easy, meaningful, and accessible to everyone in the class. Jill had stressed the importance of vocabulary acquisition, and the students were doing what they could to improve.

Jill nodded. This might just work. She'd get them used to the idea of doing a little bit of meaningful homework every day then move forward with some longer and more rigorous assignments.

Jill knew it was only a small move towards homework completion, but it was still a move. An hour later she was walking to get some coffee when Tiana walked out of her room ahead of her.

Tiana slowed down to allow Jill to join her then looked down and said, "Jill, you have that 'something is bothering me' look on your face. What is going on?"

"I'm working on building relationships with kids. But I just don't have what you have. How do I get it?" Jill asked.

Tiana smiled. "Let's walk and talk," she said. "I have to speak with a student, and I can only catch her now, in gym."

The two walked quickly together.

"If you really want to know the students you teach, you need to speak with them alone. Work with students one-on-one. Before each session, start out by asking the student a few things about his or her life outside the classroom. You have to find out what their obstacles are. Obstacles don't block our path; they *are* the path."

Jill blinked. She thought about how easy it would be to call a few students in after school and work with them individually. They passed a group of three students. Tiana gave one of the boys a fist bump on her way past him.

"After you've worked with a lot of the students one-on-one, I think you'll really see a difference in the way that your classes run."

"Why do you think that is?" Jill asked.

"Well, again, kids have a good sense of who cares about them and who doesn't. When you've worked one-on-one with a student and really invested in that kid, you'll see a difference."

They walked past the music rooms, where the sounds of instruments tuning mixed with the sounds of other musicians warming up.

"There's this other thing I've been thinking about. I heard it at lunch, and it's been bothering me," Jill said.

"What's that?"

"I heard that there were two thousand applicants for a single job at this school," Jill said to Tiana. "I mean, how do they even sort through those resumes?"

Tiana laughed. "Well, the honest truth is they probably don't, or they go through them pretty quickly. But I wouldn't get too caught up in those numbers. The fact is, the talent pool in teaching isn't very deep."

Jill looked at her skeptically.

"There just aren't that many people who are cut out to do this for a living," Tiana said, shrugging. "It takes a very special skill set to even be a mediocre teacher. Think about it for a minute. You have to be good with kids. You have to know your content area. And you have to know how to teach. When I used to go to job fairs and help interview, I would always ask young teachers which one of those three things they did the best. Do you know kids well, or do you know your content well, or do you know teaching well? Nobody is great at all three."

They passed through the broad foyer and started down a flight of stairs, and Tiana continued. "The thing to do is to find out what you're the best with. Sure, you should try to improve in all of the areas, but know which ones are your strengths. If you're going to trust in one thing, trust that if you're hard-working, kind, patient, and good with content, this career has a place for you."

Jill nodded and reflected that she'd have to think about her strengths when she had more time.

Tiana's Journal

There is so much complexity to building relationships with students, but honestly, there are concrete ways to do this. I gave you the strategy of working one-on-one with students in the hopes that you would begin to form strong relationships individually with your kids. That doesn't mean the culture of your class will be any better immediately, but you will have a stronger chance of those individuals helping you out in the larger classroom setting.

Once you've established those relationships, work to understand and validate who they are and dig deeper into what motivates them to work. Then the real challenge begins. If you have genuine love for who they are and how their stories brought them to this day, as a person, you will develop an appreciation for what makes them special.

Who will be the one who holds you accountable for creating rigor and accountability for your students? How can you keep expectations and compassion for your kids at very high levels? In the final analysis, it comes down to the culture you create in your class. You want a culture where the kids turn to you and say, "Ms. Cordera, this isn't my best work, and I think I can do better."

Make sure you are teaching them as hard as you are appreciating them. This starts with the individual students and then permeates the entire class.

Find a leader in the class. Form a relationship with that student. Trust that the other students will follow that student's example and want to follow yours too. Then branch out and get to know everyone in the class well. Relationships require an investment of time. But if we are talking about investments, building relationships is the best use of your time and energy. It's an investment that will continue to be returned to you tenfold as a teacher. Building relationships with students is a very abstract concept, but that doesn't mean that the strategies in doing so cannot be concrete.

10

"The old-timers don't even learn your name until you get tenure," the young man with the black-framed glasses and perpetual turtleneck said. "They figure so many untenured teachers either get fired or quit, that it's not worth their trouble."

Jill had walked into the cafeteria and sat at the young teacher's table, although Tiana was sitting at the table with the older women. It had been tempting to switch tables, but something in that action struck Jill as traitorous. Once you picked your table at lunch, it seemed like you should stick with it until the bitter end.

"They walk into people's classrooms, and if they don't see all of the kids at work, they give you a check mark. They do that two or three times, and if the kids aren't working, they just don't offer you a contract for next year," a young man with a bewildered look said.

"I have friends who work downtown. They actually get to go out for lunch. For an hour. Like, they actually get to walk around in the real world where there aren't students," the blonde woman said.

"What I wouldn't give for a job where you work alone in a quiet cubicle," a man in a polo-style shirt said. "I mean, you are literally never alone in this building."

Out of the corner of her eye, Jill saw Brian enter the cafeteria. He wasn't carrying a tray of food, just a laptop tucked under his arm. He walked past the group of older male teachers, but they barely raised their heads in acknowledgment. Jill made eye contact with him as Black Glasses started to speak again. He had his back to Brian, and as Brian drew closer, Black Glasses was saying ". . . that's what admin thinks, at least. Many of them have not taught in decades, but they like to think they can tell us what is—"

> We cannot let negativity be the movie that plays in our minds. We own the remote and can change the channel.

The woman with the frizzy blonde hair coughed and rolled her eyes over Black Glasses' head, and he stopped talking. The table fell into an awkward silence as Brian came up to the table.

Jill was mortified.

Had Brian heard what he had just said?

Jill felt in some way that she had betrayed him, although at this table she was little more than a spectator.

"Hey all, how's lunch today?" Brian said.

The lunch table stared blankly at him.

"Have you guys completed the reading for the orientation cohort?" Brian asked awkwardly.

Jill realized in that moment that Brian had heard what was being said when he walked up.

Jill spoke up. "I've started it," she said. "The disciplinary literacy section was pretty interesting."

The other young teachers looked at one another in silence.

"Well, I hope you have a good Wednesday," Brian said. He turned and walked out of the cafeteria quickly.

"Idiot," the blonde woman said to the young man in black glasses. "You were talking about him, and he was right there."

Black Glasses shrugged. "I mean, you could've stopped me," he said. "But who cares?"

Tiana's Journal

A school is comprised of so many people and perspectives. Some of your colleagues' perspectives will seem different from your own, and it can feel hard to find what you have in common. But the strength of the building and the kids' experience demand that we work as a team. In my career, whenever I've disappeared into my own corner and seen things only from the way I wanted to, I needlessly separated myself from valuable help, advice, compassion, and experience.

It can be difficult to sit in a room and listen, really listen, to someone else who seems to be talking in a way so different from yours. So I'll offer some practical advice: Repeat what someone tells you in the most generous light you can think of before you offer any criticism of your own. If it's practical to do it, actually repeat what they say back to them and ask them if that's what they're saying. This is some of Carl Rogers' teaching, and if you employ it, you will literally train yourself to hear what people say more clearly.

The second piece of advice is to find the center of a team, and in our case as teachers, that is the students. Remind yourself continually that we are trying to do what is best for a kid or group of kids. Err on the side of believing that everyone else is pulling for the kids and try to focus on the center—the kids. You may even try to say in a meeting, "I know we're trying to do the best for this kid, so . . ." and go on from there. Maybe what you're proposing is the best idea, or maybe it's not. Once you've failed to see around enough corners, you'll have a humility born of failure. Don't worry, that day will come.

I see you are starting to navigate the teachers' lounge, Jill. I hope you are okay over there, and I hope you feel comfortable sitting with those folks.

Sadly, I have to say your lunch table isn't filled with the most positive teachers in the building. In fact, some of those teachers act like they've never left school themselves. Most of them are decent teachers and good people overall, and that is why I cannot understand why they complain about so many things. In any profession, you will find negativity. It is important that you do not surround yourself with it.

This school is filled with tremendous teachers. Some of them might be a little "burned-out," but the love of kids and the craft of teaching is still there. Find those people. There are four kinds of people in your life: those who add, multiply, subtract, and divide. You have to hang out with the first two.

— 11 —

Jill sat at her desk while Camilla, seated in a student desk, stared at her. The final bell had rung, the noise in the hallway diminished to the point where, except for the conversations of small groups of students passing outside the open door, the building was quiet.

Camilla sat with her arms crossed across her chest.

"I don't know why I had to come in today. If you can't teach everything during class, why should I have to come after school?"

Jill nodded and registered the remark.

"I was thinking that I could help you with your studying and maybe get to know you a bit," Jill said simply.

"Seeing me every day in class isn't enough?" Camilla asked. She stared at Jill and seemed to relax her defiant posture just a bit.

"What do you do when you're not here?" Jill asked.

"Nothing," Camilla said.

"Okay, so what does nothing look like?"

"Nothing. You know, like chill at the crib. I'm on my phone a lot."

"So chilling at your crib," Jill said, and both she and Camilla smiled ever so slightly at Jill's use of the slang. "What's that about?"

"I don't know. Just sit on the couch, and sometimes I watch movies on the computer."

"What have you seen recently that's good?" Jill asked.

"Man, I saw this movie, *The Hate You Give*. I literally cried throughout the entire thing."

"Really? Why was that?" Jill asked.

Camilla dropped her arms and then smacked the open palm of her left hand with the back of her right.

"That stuff was just so *real*. It's like, that's how people get treated in our society. I was just kind of amazed that they even made the movie."

"Wait," Jill said, "Why were you amazed that someone put it on the screen?"

"Because people just don't make movies about the way my life is," Camilla said.

"And what way is that?" Jill asked.

Camilla relaxed into the desk and looked up at the ceiling.

And then she started to talk.

Throughout what Camilla said, despite the fact that she saw things in a way very different than the way Jill would have viewed them, she painted a portrait of a life that Jill could understand.

Camilla's parents both worked two jobs, and much of the responsibility for caring for her younger brother and sister fell to Camilla. On her way back home from school, she had to pick up her two younger siblings, get them home and feed them, and then entertain them until one of her parents came home to put them to bed.

"When do you do your homework?" Jill asked Camilla.

Camilla shrugged.

"Sometimes I put my brother and sister in front of the television just to make them be quiet so that I can do some schoolwork. I know they shouldn't be watching television all the time, but I have to study."

> Teachers carry two buckets: one filled with gasoline and one filled with water. It's important to use the right bucket with the right students.

Jill thought back on some of the assignments she'd seen from Camilla. If she were being honest, Jill had to admit that given the circumstances in which they were created, they were actually pretty good.

"If I had all of your responsibilities, I would never do as well as you in school," Jill said.

Camilla laughed. "You don't think so? You get the hang of it. I mean, most of the time my brother and sister are pretty cool. Sometimes they fight and stuff, but they know that I have to work hard at school."

It had never occurred to Jill that Camilla actually was working hard. It was just Camilla's schedule that was holding her back from doing really great work.

"And I work at KFC on the weekends," Camilla said.

"Really?" Jill asked. "You have a part-time job?"

"I mean, it's not that many hours. On Saturdays and Sundays, I usually work about eight hours."

"Four hours each day?" Jill asked.

"No, eight hours a day," Camilla corrected her.

"So you put in sixteen hours over the weekend working?" Jill asked. She shook her head. "Okay, so the first thing is, if you work this hard in ordinary life, you will be a success," Jill said. "Between going to school, caring for your younger brother and sister, and working at KFC, you're putting in the kind of hours that make somebody a successful professional."

Camilla shook her head.

"No, I just don't have those kinds of brains," she said. "You know that PowerPoint you were showing us on Tuesday? There is no way I could understand that like you do."

"That's just because I've read, like, fifty books on the topic," Jill said.

"I still couldn't understand it like you do," Camilla said.

"Um, I really think you'd be surprised," Jill said and laughed.

"Okay," Camilla said and rolled her eyes.

"We should probably get to the part where I help you on your homework," Jill said. Camilla smiled, opened up her notebook, and placed it on the desk.

"Okay, let's do it," Camilla said.

—— 12 ——

"How did it go today in your early classes?" Tiana asked as she and Jill walked together toward the front office.

"I can't say that it's going really, really well. But there are a few students who are just beginning to start to try. Nothing great so far," Jill said.

"Is there a kid in there who has come alive in the last few days?" Tiana asked.

"Yeah, there's this kid, Jimmy. He's been raising his hand, and he's given some good answers. At the beginning of the year, he would just stare at his desk, zoned out. It's kind of nice to see him start to care," Jill said.

Tiana stopped walking and turned to face Jill.

"So one of the things that you can do to make an enormous difference in a kid's life is to call home with good news. If this kid Jimmy has come alive in the last few days, you should call home and simply express that."

Jill nodded. She looked at the envelope she was carrying.

"I'll do that as soon as I put this in the mailroom," she said.

"I'll take it down for you," Tiana said. "You go make that call."

Jill went back to her classroom, looked up the contact information for Jimmy and dialed his mom's number.

"What's he done now?" Mrs. Greenberg asked when Jill identified herself.

"No, no, it's nothing like that," Jill said hurriedly. "I just wanted to call to tell you that Jimmy has really been trying in class lately. At the beginning of the year, he had some trouble focusing, but in the last few days, he's given some good answers, and he actually seems like he is enjoying being in class. I really appreciate the extra effort that he's putting in."

There was a pause at the other end of the phone. Jill was slightly embarrassed at having called a parent and bothered her in the middle of the afternoon just to give her news that was in no way actionable.

"Thank you so much for calling," Mrs. Greenberg said. "I've received dozens of phone calls over the years about my three boys, and this is the first one that was good news." The woman laughed. "I can't believe you called me about something positive. Thank you."

Jill hung up and walked over to Tiana's room. She'd asked Tiana if she could observe her class, and she walked into the room just ahead of the students and slid into a student desk at the back of the room.

Jill knew that she would be watching this class with new eyes. She had never watched a great teacher work while she herself was involved in trying to get better as a teacher.

Tiana stood out in the hallway greeting the students one by one as they entered the classroom. Jill paid attention to the conversations.

"Good morning, Mrs. Williams," said a tall girl in sweatpants.

"Good morning, Andrea," Tiana said. "How was the game last night?"

"I mean, I played well, but we still lost. They're really good."

Tiana murmured something that Jill didn't catch.

The girl entered the classroom, and Jill heard Tiana speak to a boy who spoke to her while looking at his feet.

"Are you ready to go today, Jesus?" Tiana was asking.

"I think I am," the boy replied. "I had to work last night, but after work I spent an hour going over the documents like you showed me. I made notes, and I think I understand it."

"Nice. Can I look at those notes later on?" Tiana asked.

"Sure, but my handwriting is pretty sloppy," Jesus said.

"So's mine," Tiana said. "And I'm happy that you spent the time even after you worked, Jesus."

The last of the students entered the room, and the bell rang. Jill had the feeling that she was about to witness something special, the nature of which was still unclear to her. The students talked quietly among themselves. Tiana stood, relaxed, at the front of the room, smiling. She said something to a girl in the front row quietly, and Jill was just able to pick up what she said.

"Are we going hard today, or are we going to take it easy?" Tiana asked.

Jill missed what the small girl said, but Tiana nodded vigorously at whatever it was.

"Okay then, let's do it," Tiana said. She clapped her hands once, and the classroom became completely silent. Jill wondered how Tiana was going to introduce the lesson.

"Does anyone have anything that they want to say before we get started?" Tiana asked.

The students looked up at her in silence, until one boy raised his hand. Tiana nodded at him.

"I was at work yesterday, and some of the people I work with said that our manager isn't very good, and they are going to ask the other manager if I can move up and be a manager," the boy said.

When a student reflects on what they remember from your class ten years ago, what will they remember most? Culture > Everything.

"Nice," Tiana said. "First of all, let's give it up for Roger."

The class broke into loud applause, and Tiana's was the loudest of all. Tiana asked Roger a few questions, and he gave short replies, but Jill could see clearly that the boy was full with pride.

She was struck by the directness of Tiana's gaze and her questions. For those short moments, it was as if this boy was at the very center of Tiana's world, and nothing else existed. Then, as quickly as it had begun, the conversation was over. Tiana scanned the room.

"Anything else you want to chat about before class starts?" Tiana asked. The class was silent. "No? Okay, let's do it."

She nodded ever so slightly, and suddenly the room was alive with students moving their desks into groups of four. Tiana walked to her desk, seemingly oblivious to the action in the room. She flipped open her laptop, scanned something on the screen, clicked a few times, and shut the lid.

The students brought out packets of paper and their laptops, and suddenly they were involved in specific, deep analysis.

"So the point that you made yesterday about the evidence in the second article was a good one," a boy near Jill was saying. "I mean, I think that the evidence here actually supports a different position, and so I think that we should use it for the end of our presentation."

"No, I think you're wrong," a girl in his group said. Suddenly, Tiana was standing right next to the group.

"Alexis," Tiana said to the girl, "we all really want to hear what you have to say, and I love your energy, but could you acknowledge Ron's comment before you jump in?"

"I'm sorry, Ron," Alexis said. "And I do think that the evidence in the second article is solid, but I also think that it supports the thesis that this author, what's her name, is making."

Across the room, Jill could hear another group talking loudly.

"That's not even relevant!" A small boy was almost shouting. "And that's not even a good source!"

Again, Tiana moved quickly through the class, and although her words were obscured by other conversations in the room, the group quieted down, and the boy who had spoken sharply nodded, acknowledging something that Tiana had said.

The room was alive with activity, and at times the conversations seemed loud and even heated, but Jill was aware that the students were reading, analyzing, and debating without any significant direction in the moment by Tiana. Jill wondered how Tiana had gotten the class to engage this deeply and passionately in a topic. At the exact moment Jill had this thought, she watched Tiana walk to the middle of the room, turn, and stare out the window.

She held this gaze for a moment, but then she was moving again across the room.

She stood next to the boy, Jesus, who had spoken to her on his way into the class. She bent over his notes, asking him questions, and pointing to specific places in his work. Then she clapped her hands once, and the classroom became silent.

"I know, I know, you want to keep talking, but I just wanted to take a minute to acknowledge something that Jesus did here. He stayed up late, after work, and finished up these notes, and let me tell you something, they are really well done. So let's give it up for Jesus!"

> You show me a great classroom culture, and I'll show you a great teacher.

The class broke into applause, and although Jesus was squirming awkwardly, Jill could see that he appreciated the acknowledgment. The groups went back to their work, and Tiana stood by the windows listening to two of the groups, moving between them to hear what the students were saying. Tiana herself remained silent until a girl, pointing at the screen of her laptop, asked Tiana a question.

"Do you want me to just answer that, or can I do some teaching here?" Tiana asked the girl.

The girl laughed. "Could you just tell me?" The girl answered. "I've been looking at this for fifteen minutes, and I still can't figure it out."

"That author is hiding his main point down in the last two paragraphs," Tiana said. "Now, there are a lot of reasons why a writer would do this, but my sense is that he is doing it because he realizes that his thesis isn't that strong and that the real appeal of the whole piece is in the details at the beginning."

The girl nodded, and Jill could see her scrolling down the page.

"I want you to read that last part and tell me if you think I'm right," Tiana said.

Tiana withdrew from the group and walked slowly over to a group that had grown silent. Jill heard the tail end of a question that Tiana asked, and then one of the students started summarizing the argument of an article on her desk.

Suddenly a bell rang, and Jill jumped a little. She wondered if it was a fire drill, but then she checked the big wall clock and realized that the period was over.

"Thank you, ladies and gentlemen," Tiana called over the noise. "Anthony, if you would do the honors, please?"

A boy wearing a hockey jersey hurried to the door and opened it, and then he stood by the door. Every student gave him a special handshake as they left the room. For some, it was a simple fist bump. For others, it was an involved handshake. Others just did a simple gesture. When everyone had cleared the room, Anthony walked over to Tiana and gave her a fist bump. Then he walked out of the room, leaving Tiana and Jill in the room alone.

"That was great," Jill said.

Tiana thanked her, and Jill looked at her for moment, unsure as to what she should say.

"I'm going to have to ask you some questions about how you did that, but right now, I've got to teach," Jill said.

Tiana laughed.

"Go get 'em," she called out as Jill rushed out the door.

13

Brian had formally observed Jill's second period two days before. As she walked into his office, she didn't know what to expect. Jill knew that formal evaluations from the administration were important, and often those observations were the only documented evidence to determine summative evaluations at the end of the year.

She thought that the lesson had gone well. She wondered whether her familiarity with him would make it easier or harder for Brian to be professional about feedback. Would some of her earlier, more unguarded moments influence how the evaluation would go?

The minute that Jill sat down opposite Brian and looked at his impeccably neat desk and his stiff posture, she knew this would be a formal observation meeting. Everything in his office seemed to be either black or white. The phone, the computer, and all of the pens were black, and the walls were white. Jill felt conflicted about the formality of the meeting since she had seen a more human side of Brian at Taft's that first week of school.

"Thank you for having me in your class the other day," Brian said. He smiled to himself and then said, "Sorry, I know that the choice wasn't really yours, but I did like being there."

Jill started to relax. Maybe this was not going to be as painful as she had imagined it would be. She had faith that Brian was, if nothing else, professional.

"Let me just start out with a running narrative of what happened in the class, and then we can get to the part where I make recommendations and kind of give you a sense of where this particular lesson would fall in the framework."

While Brian was in the classroom, Jill had noticed that he never once stopped typing. Although his eyes almost never left the screen of his laptop, she was sure that he was observing the classroom closely.

"If at any point I'm saying something that you don't think happened, or happened in another way, please tell me, and I'll make a note of it," Brian said.

Suddenly, Jill felt like she was in some sort of official proceeding, like a law case, where words had meanings other than their common ones.

Brian began to read his notes.

"The class opened with a brief discussion about the lesson from the previous day. Ms. Cordera asked the students to read the first two paragraphs of chapter three and highlight and define the important vocabulary words from the passage. After the class discussed which words they chose, Ms. Cordera instructed the class to take notes while she went through some slides on the smartboard. Ms. Cordera told some interesting stories about the topic, and the students listened but didn't take notes during story time. The class ended with an explanation of the homework, which was to answer the three questions at the end of the reading that night."

"I think we should start out by saying that for a first year teacher, this lesson was pretty good," said Brian. "We want you to learn and grow and be willing to improve, and this was a good start."

Jill didn't know whether she should feel relieved or worried about what he had just said.

"So one of the things I noticed is that there was a lot of *you* at the front of the room, telling the students what to do and think. At this point, I think it's fair to say that almost the entire lesson I watched was teacher-centered," Brian said.

Jill started to squirm a bit in her chair. If the narrative had left her wondering whether Brian had viewed her lesson in a negative light, his first critique left no doubt that she was in for some pointed evaluation. When she was planning the lesson, she had not thought about whether it was a teacher-centered or student-centered.

"Can you tell me a little more about what teacher-centered means? I don't understand," Jill said. "To me, the students had to read, respond, take notes, and listen during the lesson. It seems like the students were doing a lot."

"That's right," responded Brian. "The students *were* doing a lot, but only because you told them to. We want our students to read, write, think, analyze, synthesize, corroborate, and wrestle with the content. Ideally, the students create their own moments for themselves within your structure. While your lesson had some moments like that, it was all about you."

"What do you mean, 'all about me'?" Jill asked.

Brian paused. He seemed to think for a moment.

"When you teach, it's sort of like 'your stage, their show,'" he said slowly. "Your stage should be organized and laid out the way you want it to be. Your stage set-up should follow specific directions and protocols that you establish as the teacher. But once the show starts, it's theirs. They need to be the actors, the drama, and the intrigue. They need to be the creators of content and thought.

So how can you get yourself to a place where I can see this in your room?"

Jill thought for a few seconds. She understood his analogy now, but after struggling with classroom management and setting a purpose for the lesson, she still felt uneasy about turning over control to the students.

Evaluation is all about attitude. The evaluator is mainly looking at how you will respond. Listen to understand and reflect on the feedback's purpose.

"I think I know what you mean," said Jill. "But I couldn't really tell you how I'd start to do that. Do you have any suggestions?"

"I appreciate that you are asking questions, Jill," Brian responded. "When you give notes, can you write them in the form of questions instead of statements and have the students formulate the answers? When you told that story at the end, could you have given the students some parameters and had them act out the story in front of the class? Maybe the students could create their own notes and then compare them with yours and with one another. All of these are ways to have them star in the show. You have to be the 'guide on the side,' not the 'sage on the stage.'"

He's right, she thought. *All of this sounds really hard to do, but he is right.*

Her lesson wasn't a failure, but she knew it could be improved. *I need to notice what an administrator notices,* she thought.

"I also think there were some great moments—" Brian stopped and coughed lightly into his hand.

Jill leaned forward, thinking that he was about to say something positive.

"I'm sorry about that," Brian said, clearing his throat. "There were some really great moments when you could have addressed at least two of the building goals. Those building goals were outlined in our district in-service day at the beginning of the year, and they have been reiterated throughout the semester in your department meetings."

Brian looked at her for a moment in silence. He seemed to be waiting for Jill to say something, but she couldn't think of what that might be.

"Talk to me about how you've incorporated them into your lessons this year," Brian asked.

"Um, I think I have a general idea of what they are, but I can't say they've been a top priority for me in my classes," Jill said.

Brian nodded. "Well, if those building goals haven't been properly articulated, on some levels that's my fault. So let's walk through them together. At the first faculty meeting, we talked about how we want students to be given challenging texts to read. This will help them on their standardized tests. When we give readers a text, we aren't doing them any favors if we ask them to read something below grade level. Have you used any metrics to figure out the reading level of the homework you assigned them?"

Jill looked at her hands for a quick moment before answering.

"Sorry," said Jill. "I think you already know the answer to that."

"Again, that is okay, but we are asking that all of our teachers really select appropriate texts because it makes a big difference," Brian remarked. "And our second goal pairs really well with that. The students should practice the skills tested on the state and national assessments at the end of the year."

Jill thought quickly about how some teachers had reacted at the beginning of the year when the new initiative had been launched. Many of them felt that the goals were too "test-preppy" and took the focus away from their curriculum.

Student outcomes are about students, not outcomes.

"I have nothing to say," Jill muttered. "I've been struggling so hard to keep my head above water that . . ." She trailed off. She felt overwhelmed by the number of things she needed to focus on. "I really haven't been overly selective about teaching the right texts and skills to students, much less putting them at the center of my design. I'm really sorry."

"I get it," said Brian. "Having said that, your students under-stand your purpose, and they aren't fighting you about the real reason that they're with you."

Brian stopped for a moment and looked purposely at Jill. Jill thought that she should say something, so she said, "Thank you."

"Not a lot of teachers can do that in their first semester as a teacher," Brian said. "It's nice to see. The students obviously really like you. I am not sure if you noticed this, but when you were setting up your computer, one of your students was chatting with another saying, 'I can tell she's nervous today, but she shouldn't be. She just has to be herself.'"

"It's kind of weird that they were talking about me in my classroom with you right there, and literally behind my back," Jill said, laughing.

"Sure," said Brian. "But the point is that I think they care about you. It's an acknowledgment that 'being yourself' is good enough for them. And for me too, quite frankly."

Jill looked at Brian and nodded. He had said so many things that she would need time to unpack it all.

Then the bell rang, signaling the end of the period, and they both stood.

14

Jill sat at the kitchen table in her apartment with her computer open in front of her, some examples of articles on the table, and a spiral notebook leaning up against a textbook. Jill tried to remember Brian's comments about her class. She wrote down the words that he had used in order.

Read, write, think, analyze, synthesize, corroborate.

The other thing he'd said was that she should use challenging texts.

Okay, she thought. *Let's start with challenging texts.*

She selected one of the articles and opened up the Lexile tool. She quickly typed in a paragraph from the middle of the piece. The Lexile number popped up. She compared it to the grade level it was supposed to correspond to.

Whoa! Too low. Not even close, she thought.

She grabbed another article and did the same thing. This piece seemed to fit the grade level.

Okay, now all I have to do is get them to write something about it, and I've crossed two things off the list. Actually, three, because they can't write unless they're thinking.

She looked at the third word Brian had used. Analyze.

If I have them analyze something and write about it, that would be four things off the list, she thought.

She wrote instructions on a separate piece of paper. "Analyze the way that this author makes her case for the importance of this issue."

She looked at the next word that Brian had used.

Synthesize.

She looked for another article with an opposing perspective. She glanced at it then discarded it as too easy for the students. Then she looked at her instructions again. "Analyze the way that this author makes her case for the importance of this issue and use evidence from both articles to argue that one author presents the stronger case."

She looked back at the list of words Brian had used. It looked to her like she was using all of them.

An administrator sees my class in different ways than I do, she thought. How do I make it less about me at the front of the room and more about the kids?

Although Brian's standards seemed too high to her, what he had said was right.

Maybe I could have them working in groups after they've read this piece. Then I could have them present their arguments. Jill shrugged. It's not genius, but maybe it doesn't have to be.

She checked the Lexile level on the second article and typed up the instructions. The next thing that Brian said was that the class had to prepare the students for standardized tests. Jill went online and looked at the questions that the state would use on the test in the spring.

"What is the main idea of the article?" the first question asked.

Jill wrote a section on each of the articles where the students had to define the main idea. After she was finished writing the outline, she closed her laptop.

Well, at least I'm responding to what he said, Jill thought. *Let's see if it works.*

Stubbornness feels heavy and negative and will drag you down. Determination feels light, is positive, and will take you far.

15

"I'm just really happy for you that you spent so much time and effort on this paragraph," Jill said to a boy dressed in an enormous football jersey. She underlined a sentence on the boy's paper. "Your writing is so much clearer than it used to be. You have solid evidence right here. You know how to do this, so can you write another paragraph and let me take a look at it tomorrow?"

The boy nodded and, taking his paper off of her desk, scooped up his backpack.

"Thanks, Ms. Cordera," he said, and he hurried out of the classroom.

"Knock, knock," Tiana said, walking into Jill's room. "Have time to chat?"

Jill nodded and slumped back into her chair.

Tiana sat down in a student desk by Jill.

"How did that conference with Brian go?" Tiana asked.

"I had no idea that there was so much to teaching," Jill said. "I mean, I thought that it was going to be enough to get the students working in class. But now I have to make it *student-centered.*

I seriously didn't even know what that meant. He had to explain it to me."

Tiana held out her hand to stop Jill.

"Brian's comments are designed to make you a better teacher, and, sure, in order to get really, really good at teaching, those are the things you should focus on. If he gives you a perfect evaluation in the first semester of your first year, what will you have to work toward? There are some things you need to improve on. We all have those things."

It's hard to understand what you cannot see. It is important to always have one person in your life who is your accountability partner and your blind-spot checker.

Jill put her face in her hands. It seemed so overwhelming. *How could anyone think of all these things and still teach?*

"But let's be very clear here," Tiana said forcefully. "There are lots and lots of great teachers who teach in very traditional, teacher-centered ways, and the students absolutely love being in their classroom, and they learn a lot."

Jill looked up and put her hands flat on the desk. "Is that true?" she asked.

"It's absolutely true," Tiana said. "Look, I'm just going to say this, and I don't necessarily believe all of it, but just listen to the argument. In education, if it wasn't here yesterday, you don't need it. Because the truth is, there were a lot of people being taught really well yesterday. So that new teaching technique? That new piece of technology? That new study that found we should all be doing something other than what we're doing? All that stuff isn't that important because yesterday and the year before that and the decade before that, there were great teachers teaching really well. That new stuff? It's good to think about. But, Jill, you are doing a great job of reaching kids, especially for a new teacher. If Brian noticed that capacity in your class, that is a huge 'win' for your first evaluation."

"So why do I feel like such a failure?" Jill asked.

The difference between teachers who live up to their potential and those who don't is the willingness to look at themselves and others objectively. Listening > Ego

"It takes a lot of confidence to receive criticism well," Tiana said. "I mean, it angers me a bit when an administrator walks into my room and says something negative about my classroom. And I've been doing this for a long time. To pick up on one little thing that I did wrong? It just seems petty. But if I summon my better self, I know that I can always improve."

Jill shook her head as if to clear it. She blinked once and looked up at the ceiling. "I just want it to be simpler," she said finally.

"Okay, so let's do simple," Tiana said. "Are you moving the kids along a continuum of the three major skills that they have to improve on?"

Jill nodded quickly.

"Are they becoming better at really important, global skills?"

Again, Jill nodded quickly.

"Then you're doing your job," Tiana said.

Jill laughed in spite of herself. "Well, now I think that you're making it too simple," Jill said.

"Fine. Then demand an extra element of yourself. Take it up one notch."

Tiana tapped the desk in front of her. "Take *one* of the things that Brian said and use it in your classroom. Text complexity? Okay, let's address some of that. But know that you have to do it slowly and with purpose. And be kind to yourself. Be *kind* to yourself."

Tiana paused for a moment, and when she spoke again, it sounded almost as if she were speaking to herself. "Above all, be kind to yourself."

The two sat for a moment in silence, and Jill thought about the words Tiana had used then about the way she had used them. Jill moved slightly forward, and in that gesture, it was as if she had also changed her perspective. Tiana always appeared to her as almost above her own emotions and motivations because she was so competent at teaching. Now, listening to her speak, Jill became aware that the words Tiana had spoken held some sort of deeper meaning.

She immediately saw the older teacher in a different light, as if those simple words, "Be kind to yourself," had given Jill some sort of insight into Tiana. She suddenly saw how enormously tough on herself Tiana must have been in order to improve year after year, decade after decade.

"Listen to me very carefully," Tiana said. "Some of the best teachers I've ever taught with aren't teachers anymore," Tiana said. "They don't teach anymore. *They're not in the room with kids.* Why? Because they were too tough on themselves. They didn't know that this is a marathon, not a sprint. They didn't understand that they couldn't have a perfectly planned, innovative lesson *every single day.*"

Tiana sat absolutely still. She looked at Jill for a moment in silence.

"They. Burned. Themselves. Out!" Tiana said slowly, and at the end, her voice rose to almost a shout, and she punctuated the last word by bringing her fist down on the desk with a thud.

She paused, and when she spoke again, her voice was very quiet.

"Don't do that," she said. "Pick a few things and improve on them."

As Jill sat looking at Tiana, an unexpected feeling took hold of her. Instead of feeling overwhelmed by the number of things she would need to attend to in order to teach well, she felt invigorated by it.

She felt her spirits begin to rise. She thought of all of the teachers she had known and how some of them went to conferences during the summer, read books in their field when they weren't in the classroom, and sat around talking about teaching when they weren't actually doing it. All at once, Jill not only understood why those teachers spent their lives this way, but she also wanted to do the same.

The fear that Jill had felt constricting her when she'd sat down with Tiana left her, and in its place, she felt a sense of wonder.

"It can be fun, can't it?" Jill asked.

"What can?" Tiana asked.

"Teaching. It can actually be fun, can't it?"

Tiana smiled, and she looked at Jill full in the face. When she spoke, her voice was almost a whisper, as if the subject itself were so awe-inspiring that a quiet, reverent tone was required to describe it properly. She leaned toward Jill, and she sounded like she was telling Jill a secret when she spoke.

"Oh, Jill. You have no idea. You can't have any idea what this career has meant to me and what a whole lot of fun it has been. Just *fun*. It's an art form, and you get to create and experience and experiment, and that makes you never want to do anything else if you really love doing those things. It's also a craft, and it feels good to master a craft.

"And it will change you," she continued. "Remember? Nothing matures you more quickly or more deeply than the sustained responsibility for another person's welfare. You stop thinking about yourself as much, and you give yourself to something bigger than you could ever imagine."

Tiana shook her head, as if with disbelief, and spoke again. "I've taught maybe thirty students who went on to become teachers, and they keep in touch with me. They remind me all the time of the things we did in our classes together. Now they are doing some of the same things in their classes. It's an honor. Those were moments we created together."

Tiana looked around the classroom, as if what she was about to say next was written somewhere on the walls. Then she shook her head and looked back at Jill. Her voice became almost musical as she continued.

"I watched a younger teacher being very patient and kind with a special needs student, so of course, I went up to him and complimented what he had done. And he turned to me and said, 'I learned how to do that by watching *you*.'"

Tiana shrugged then, the palms of her hands facing upwards, and she clapped her hands together.

"What more could you ask for in a career? Or in a life?" Tiana asked.

But the questions weren't directed at Jill. It seemed she was speaking to herself.

Tiana's Journal

We just had our chat about your first evaluation today. I know it was hard for you. Think about it this way: If the administrator starts off the evaluation by saying that it was pretty good and that he saw some nice connections with students during the lesson, then you did a really good job. The rest of the feedback probably included some things you could improve on and some advice that you should take seriously. But do not lament the one or two lines in your written evaluation that may have been negative. Sometimes teachers have thin skin, and that's not so bad. It means that you care about what you're doing.

If I have learned anything about evaluation, it is this: If you want to impress an administrator, go with, "Less of the teacher, more of the students." In the end, that is good teaching too, but administrators really like to see our students shining in our classes.

They cannot see you every day, but what they do see is the way that you work. Do you contribute to the school outside the class? Are you a positive part of the school culture? Do you care about your kids? I have never seen someone fired or released from their job because of poor classroom performance alone. If you give the students everything you have, every day, and you play well in the sandbox with your colleagues, you are going to make it.

Focus on giving the kids a great experience. Students learn better when they are having fun, and so does everyone else. Create a structure where students are learning content and skills and having an incredible experience in your class. Entertain, innovate, and get to your instructional goals.

Each time you are evaluated, you have a chance to get better at your craft. Relish and capitalize on this opportunity—not with the fear of failure but with the hunger to improve.

—— 16 ——

Jill walked out into the hall from her talk with Tiana with a new sense of freedom and elation. For the first time since she began teaching, she felt she was embarking on an adventure. It wasn't that she had totally forgotten about the fear of failure that possessed her just a short time ago, but now she felt as if she were responding to a sort of call to action. She felt she was on a kind of journey— one she had just begun, but one that opened up in front of her, mysterious and beautiful.

It was at that moment she realized that she was walking toward Camilla, and the girl was looking at her with a peculiar mixture of curiosity and intensity.

"So, how did that thing go?" Camilla asked.

"How did what thing go?" Jill asked.

"You know, the thing you told me about the other day where the principal was in your room and was grading you on your teaching. What did he say?" Camilla asked.

"In teacher evaluations, it's sort of like they tell you everything that you're doing wrong. So it's strange to sit through. I felt like I was being railed on. Oh, and he's the vice principal."

As soon as the words were out of her mouth, Jill realized that she should not have spoken with such candor to a student. But Camilla just looked at Jill and nodded slowly.

"Yeah, but Ms. Cordera? You should be really happy about your teaching."

Jill frowned, and Camilla nodded enthusiastically.

"Your class is one of my favorites so far, and you're one of my favorite teachers," Camilla said.

"Camilla! What a nice thing to say," Jill said. "What is so different about my class, our class, than your other classes?"

"You actually are trying to figure out what we don't know and how to teach us. And you can actually be kind of funny at times. I mean, not hilarious or anything, but still pretty funny."

"Well, thanks for saying that," Jill said. "Sometimes I question whether or not you all are learning."

"Of course we are! Many of our classes are so boring it's ridiculous. We do these worksheets. None of them are going to help us be successful in life. Your class is fun, and I can actually see how this might help me with my future."

"Thank you, Camilla," Jill said.

"I'm not just saying that," Camilla said. "Most of the kids really like you."

Camilla nodded with finality then said, "I have to go catch my bus. See you tomorrow."

Jill thanked her again, then suddenly she was standing alone in the hallway. She looked down the hall toward the courtyard, and for a moment, she thought about the first day of school when she had walked down the hall and looked at this same view. It certainly had changed. She'd exerted her powers of adjustment, and now both the view and her sense of herself had changed. She made a mental note to think more about that later when she wasn't consumed by the pile of papers she had to grade.

— 17 —

"I think you went a little overboard," Tiana said. She was sitting across the desk from Brian in his office. The door was firmly closed.

"Don't hold back," Brian said. "Just tell me how you really feel."

Tiana smiled, but she didn't laugh.

"What is it that you're always saying? 'Win the relationship'?"

"I've been known to say that, yeah," Brian said.

"So what part of having a conference with a new teacher—who is feeling kind of shaky about her teaching—and lighting into her about some nonsense building goals, making her feel worse about being in the classroom, is winning the relationship?"

Brian raised his hands defensively. "I had to give her an honest evaluation, and I had to give her some feedback, so she has something to work toward. I didn't lay into her."

"Well, that is certainly the impression that Jill got. Based on what she said, I don't know how it possibly could have gone down any other way," Tiana said.

"I just reminded her of some things that are important on the building level, things she should think about to get better as a teacher to improve," Brian said as his voice began to rise.

"If the kids are in their seats doing productive work in the first semester of a young teacher's career, we are going to call that a win. And we are going to encourage that young teacher, so she has the confidence to get better. And you know it."

"I did encourage her," Brian said. "I told her that it was clear the students knew what was expected of them. I told her the class was good for a new teacher. I told her a nice story about how the kids reacted in her class."

"Did you win the relationship?" Tiana asked pointedly.

"Yeah, I think I did," Brian replied.

"So why was I talking to Jill for half an hour telling her that she isn't a complete failure as a teacher?" Tiana asked.

"I didn't say that!"

"I'm not saying you did. I'm just telling you what she heard," Tiana said.

"So how am I supposed to be honest and truthful and still prevent teachers from only hearing the negative?" He shook his head. "It's an honest question."

> Knowledge is knowing that a tomato is a fruit. Wisdom is knowing not to put it in a fruit basket.

"Starting out in teaching is a largely emotional process. You know that. Your nerves are raw when you're a rookie. You doubt yourself, and you're always eager for encouragement. Brian, you tried to solve an emotional problem with logic. Jill needs, emotionally *needs*, you to tell her that she's doing a good job. Put some logic in there. Absolutely. Tell her a thing or two that will make her a better teacher but realize that you don't solve logical problems emotionally, and you don't solve emotional problems logically."

Brian put his elbows on the desk and looked at Tiana for a long moment. "Okay, I see what you're saying. But I have evaluations to fill out. There are decisions to be made. I'm thinking about the institution, the school."

"So think about the school. But can I be honest with you?" Tiana said. "You skipped steps. You went in cold for an evaluation, and you hadn't done any coaching beforehand. You didn't debrief over her informal evaluation. You haven't talked to her after school to find out what's going on with her, and you went in there and made a teacher who can actually relate to kids feel bad."

Tiana stopped talking for a moment, and Brian slumped back in his chair.

"That wasn't my intention," he said.

"Brian, I know it wasn't your intention. What do you think I take you for? I'm just saying how it felt to Jill," Tiana said. "You may have thought that you gave her some good advice, but how much time did you really spend complimenting the good things she was doing? A person can survive on a good compliment for several weeks, and sometimes teachers have to. If she did something wrong, point it out. But she is starting to do some things right, and you should be going crazy to celebrate. That is how to build people up instead of tear them down."

Brian fidgeted a little and looked at his hands. "Okay. You're right. I screwed up. I do like Jill, and I think she has potential. How do I fix it?" he asked.

Tiana paused. She took a deep breath and settled back in her chair.

"Have you forgotten?" Tiana asked quietly. "Have you forgotten how hard it is to begin teaching? There are so many things to learn and so many things that demand your attention. Even when you're winning, it feels like you're not because there is always the next thing, the next lesson plan, the next student who needs extra help, and you haven't yet gotten a chance to weigh those things against the positive, beautiful things that you can do in a classroom. When you're young, you haven't seen anything come to fruition yet. In your first year, you're just in there fighting without any sense of proportion or perspective. It's the people around you, those lifelines of colleagues, who give you the strength to go on."

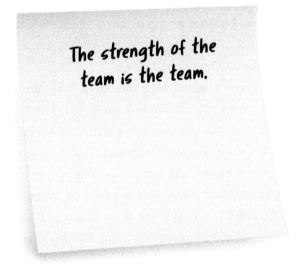

The strength of the team is the team.

Brian was looking at Tiana and listening intently. When she finished, he put his face in his hands for a moment. Then he looked at her.

"Tell me a story about when you were a young teacher," Tiana said quietly.

Brian laughed and waved his hand around his office.

"Do you mean I'm supposed to remember something before all this happened?" Brian asked, finally pointing at a pile of manila folders next to the phone.

"Yes, let's just keep it real, shall we?" Tiana said.

Brian smiled.

"Well, I was hired with five other teachers in my department. I was doing okay, but I was coaching, getting my act together in the classroom, and I was getting married that summer, so there were a lot of plans to be made. I'd had some average informal evaluations, and my department chair was doing this thing where he would play the young teachers off each other."

"What do you mean?" Tiana asked.

"Oh, you know, he'd walk in on Monday morning and say, 'I just observed so-and-so, and he's doing really great things in the classroom. What a great teacher!' And then he'd go on and on about the innovative things that this person was doing. It made me feel like if I was anything less than John Dewey, I was just barely hanging on."

Brian laughed and shook his head, remembering.

"So how did that make you feel?" Tiana asked.

"I felt like I should be sending my resume out to another school," Brian said. "But wait, that isn't the worst part. The department chair would always keep this black notebook with him, and he was always writing in it. It was weird because it didn't even seem like he was writing sentences. The thing looked like a ledger book."

"Some sort of tally sheet?" Tiana asked.

Brian nodded. "That's the way it seemed. But here is the strange thing. One afternoon I was in the department office grading papers at one end of that long table they have in there. And this guy's ledger book was open at the end of the table. I mean, it was almost as if the guy had left the book there for me to take a look at."

Brian paused. "This next part is kind of embarrassing," he said.

"What? You looked in the book, right?" Tiana asked.

"Of course I looked in the book! Part of me thinks he left it there for me to look at," Brian said.

"He probably did," Tiana said.

"Yeah, so I looked in the book, and sure enough, there were these rows, like columns. They all had headings: my name and five other teachers. Then there were these categories, like, 'Content knowledge. Presence. Attitude. Does he or she get along with me? Extra stuff around school. Potential for growth.' I kid you not. I can't remember them all, but there were ten categories listed, and each of the new teachers was ranked on a five-point scale. I added up all my points, and I was ranked fifth out of the six new teachers in the department that year."

"That must've made you feel horrible," Tiana said.

"On a number of different levels," Brian said. "Part of me, a big part of me, felt good for the other teachers. Another part of me felt like there was no way I would ever be able to teach well. I'd never really measure up if you put me alongside other teachers."

Brian stopped talking, and for a moment the two of them sat in the office in silence. Tiana looked out the window and saw the great mass of students leaving school for the day. Brian looked at her and then followed her eyes. He swiveled his chair and looked out the window, resting an elbow on the desk.

"It's a funny thing about people," Tiana said. "We do all of these things to help them," she said, pointing at the students leaving the school, "and sometimes it's strange what that effort will do to you. All of this," she said, waving her hand around the office, "to help them."

They sat in silence for another moment.

"Do you want to know another funny thing?" Brian asked.

Tiana nodded.

"That guy? My department chair? He wasn't a bad guy. He had a good heart. He wanted the best for the kids, and he thought that keeping a ledger book was the right way to go."

Tiana laughed. "Brian, do you want to know what your best characteristic is?"

"I'm pretty sure you're going to tell me," Brian said.

Tiana laughed.

Seeing the best in others oftentimes helps us find the best in ourselves.

"You're right. I am," she said. "You see the best in people. You really try to see everything that a person can offer, and then you turn with a distinct judgment in their favor. You see the best in them. The best in people."

"Thank you, Tiana," Brian said. "Now, what do I do about Jill? I screwed up."

"If you just tell her that, then try to make it right, you will have done a great thing," she said.

Brian stared at Tiana for a moment. His gaze had such intensity that Tiana shrugged her shoulders.

"What?" Tiana asked.

"Did I just turn into the guy with a ledger book?" Brian asked.

Tiana laughed. "Yeah, but just for a minute. You've still got time," she said.

18

Jill's classroom was flooded with sunlight, and the students sat in groups of four looking attentively up at the smartboard. Jill looked back at them with a smile on her face and a feeling of genuine excitement about the lesson. As she looked at her students, she thought about Brian's words about how to set the stage and then let the students deliver the show. If it worked, this lesson would do exactly that.

When Jill told Tiana that she was going to do a collaborative project with another school, Tiana immediately asked if she could observe, and Jill had said yes with a nervous laugh—with the provision that Tiana not judge Jill's teaching too harshly. So Tiana sat behind Jill's desk calmly looking out at the classroom.

"This is what we're going to do," Jill said to the class. "Today we are going to make a bunch of new friends, spend some time on social media, and learn a little along the way. How does that sound?"

None of the students spoke, but they were all paying attention.

"Remember those blogs you guys wrote last week?" Jill asked. "Today, we've received a set of blogs from my teacher friend who lives in New York. His students are learning the same material you are. They wrote blogs on the same topic, and we are going to read their work. After you finish reading the blog I assign you, I would like you to leave one comment and one question for each of his students. Sound good?"

Tiana continued to observe the students. She opened up her computer and sent an instant message to Brian: "I think Jill is about to teach an awesome lesson right now. If you are free, come join us."

Again, none of the students spoke, but some nodded, and the entire class began to log on to their computers and check the links Jill had sent them. Each student received a unique link leading them to a blog written by one of the students in New York.

"At the end of it, I'd like you to have read a bunch of different blogs. You can build your knowledge of what is happening in our chapter by reading all of them. I am also interested to see if you gain a different perspective by reading something that did not come from one of your classmates."

As the students began to read and comment, some started to react with excitement.

"Someone named Kyler commented on my blog!" shouted one student.

"Sam asked me a question about my supporting details. He gave me a really good suggestion about using evidence," said another.

For a moment, Jill stood still looking at the class. It was happening just as she had planned, and she paused a moment to take it all in. She could feel her teaching shift just a bit, as she'd taken Brian's comments and made them real in her classroom.

For the rest of the period, the students typed on their computers, going back and forth between their own blogs and the blogs of the students in New York. Jill went to her laptop and opened a dashboard. She scanned the blogs quickly and smiled. Some blogs had threads of conversations that were pages long. Most of the comments were constructive and academic.

> Technology can make good teachers great—and bad teachers worse. Technology cannot be used as a pacifier or a babysitter. It has to engage, energize, and enhance what we are doing in class.

Jill looked up from her computer, and she saw Brian standing across the room, looking at a student's screen. She had not seen him come in, and the students were so focused on what they were doing that they hadn't noticed him either.

Jill walked through the classroom listening in on the conversations happening around the room.

One of the students looked up from his computer. "It's cool that someone else is reading my writing besides you, Ms. Cordera."

She threaded her way through the groups of desks, and she saw the students writing for real people in real situations. It seemed to be changing the way the students thought about what they were doing. The kids were building perspective with students one thousand miles away.

Is this what they mean by "authentic writing task"? she wondered. *It sure feels authentic.*

Tiana watched from behind Jill's desk with a smile on her face.

The room was alive with activity, and Jill thought for a moment that the students were being much more productive than they would have been if she had been standing at the front of the room. They were deeply and meaningfully productive. She thought again about Brian's suggestion to set the stage and let the students perform.

There is something to that, Jill thought. *And now he's seeing me do it.*

As the period came to an end, only Jill noticed what time it was. The students were looking at their computer screens, paying close attention as they read comments or typed their own.

"We only have a few minutes left, so try to wrap up your thoughts," Jill said loudly.

And then the unthinkable happened. A noise arose from the classroom that Jill had only thought about before but never actually believed would happen. It was a groan from some of the students—not because Jill had asked the class to do something, but because the class was ending!

"I'm just getting started!" a girl named Samantha said. "I just got a reply to what I wrote, and I feel like I'm going to let her down if I don't respond."

"Can you make a little time tonight to do that?" Jill asked. "She'll probably be waiting for a reply. I mean, I don't want to guilt trip you, but . . ."

"No, I get you," Samantha replied. "It's fine. I'll write her tonight."

The class ended with a scramble of closing computers and backpacks being swung onto shoulders.

Jill started to say something to the entire class, but then she stopped. She just stood still, savoring the feeling of having done something inarguably well. She looked over at Tiana, and Tiana nodded once emphatically before gathering her things and leaving. Her meaning was clear. Jill had done it. Jill turned around, and she saw Brian walking slowly through the maze of student desks. He was smiling.

"That was great, Jill. Not just great, but *really* great."

"Thank you, Brian," Jill said. "It's nice of you to say."

"No, thank *you* for showing me some great teaching. It really brightened my day," he said. "And there's something else I have to talk to you about."

He was standing in front of Jill, and in a gesture that seemed very unlike him, he shuffled his feet a bit and looked down at them.

"I made a mistake in the way I handled the observation I did in your class. I realize now that I was overly specific and perhaps even negative in my comments," he said. "There are things that you, that *all* of us, can work on, but I wanted you to know I think you're doing a great job, and I'd like to say I'm sorry if I made it seem that you're doing anything other than a great job."

Jill took a step backward.

"I didn't think that anything you said was too harsh or anything," she said. "I know there are things I need to work on, and you pointed them out. Thank you."

Brian smiled. "Okay. I'm glad I got a chance to see your teaching today. Let's talk about how this lesson fits in with what you're aiming for in this class. I'd like to see how you're thinking about things. And again, thank you."

And just like that, he was gone.

Jill looked at the empty room. Feeling this silence, after teaching a great lesson, seemed almost overpowering. She walked back to her desk and sat down, both exhausted and satisfied.

19

Tiana walked out of the school at the end of the day, still trying to process what she had seen in Jill's room. It was easy for her to forget that the computers on the students' desks weren't just window dressing for a skill that could be accessed with pen and paper. The activity Jill's students had done today helped them develop entirely new skills.

Tiana assigned reflection activities for students to write in their notebooks, which was a kind of blog, but Jill's activity was read by other students online. The conversation was initiated and created by students. It was all happening live, and Jill was monitoring all the posts.

Tiana had never before seen a classroom where the students were being asked to synthesize information from a point of view different from their own and do all of this in real time, speaking with people who lived across the country. Tiana walked to her car thinking about using technology in the classroom to foster global citizenship, something she had heard at professional development workshops but never really seen implemented until today.

What will this new technology do to the way we see ourselves, our communities, even our countries? she thought.

Tiana got in her car and started the engine. Sitting there, she worried that she was not keeping up with technology. She had made the transition to having students write papers on their laptops and using the teacher dashboard to leave comments for them. Those comments were more efficient because the students could read them the minute they were made, rather than waiting until the next day to get feedback.

> Technology is not bad for kids. Bad teaching is bad for kids.

But seeing Jill in the classroom that day reminded Tiana there was an entirely different world being created in the classroom by technology, and Tiana didn't know much about it.

As she pulled onto the broad avenue leading to the freeway, Tiana wondered if it was too late to join the revolution. It seemed like every year the school had a new platform for the teachers to use in order to deliver their curriculum, and the result of all of these changes was students who were confused about where to find information about their classes.

One of the comments Tiana heard repeatedly from students was that her class was easy, and at first, Tiana was annoyed at this comment. Then she asked students what they meant by it.

A serious girl with braids had told her, "In your class, we just learn what we have to know. We don't have to spend a bunch of time looking for the information."

"Do you spend a lot of time looking for information in your other classes?" Tiana had asked.

"At least a quarter of my time is spent figuring out where the teacher posts the information that I need and where to put my work," the girl replied and then shrugged. "I guess that's just what has to happen, but it seems like a waste of time."

As Tiana slipped further and further behind the technology curve, she used every rationale to describe how she felt about it. But there was no escaping the fact that it had overrun her. On her way home that day, she made a commitment to herself to go to a technology seminar that summer. There were so many ways she could use technology to make something absolutely new in her classroom.

She was still deep in thought when she opened the front door of her condominium, set her bags on the floor and sat down on her couch. She knew she needed to reach out to someone who was familiar with this new technology in order to begin her journey to creating a digital classroom.

Tiana thought about how hard she had worked when she was a young teacher, staying up late to grade everything that the kids gave her, providing feedback to every assignment they turned in. Now, she didn't need to work as hard because she did a better job from the front of the room. The kids knew what they needed to do, and they did it because they bought into a system.

But there was something that bothered Tiana about what she was doing now. Although she was doing a fine job and she had a stack of thank you notes from kids whose lives she'd changed, she was still leaving talent on the table.

Now, instead of fighting with curriculum, or even the kids, she could use the extra energy she was saving to furnish the kids with a vision of their future, maybe to suggest that they take an extra class or offer them guidance in other areas of their lives.

But she wasn't doing that.

No one would ever know but her.

She was so high on the learning curve that there was absolutely no one to take her to task. In fact, everyone told her she worked too hard. But she knew. She knew on the days when she was phoning it in that she could do better. She knew the students who needed her, who would fall through the cracks without her, were not being engaged in the same way they had been before.

Tiana thought back to a moment from her childhood, when she had been a good soccer player at twelve years old. A friend of hers played forward with her, and they practiced so much together that it was as if they could anticipate each other's moves. They had been matched one hot, cloudless, Saturday morning with a traveling team from Europe.

The other players were older, faster, stronger, and they played right on the edge of dirty. They hadn't done anything that the referee picked up, but one girl cut inside without the ball and clipped Tiana's hip. On another play, the European team had set a screen for a pass, but the referee hadn't called anything. Tiana pushed, fought, and traded trash talk all game until the final whistle blew, mercifully, on an 8-0 loss. Tiana had stumbled off the field and fallen on her back, staring up, almost sightless, at the blue sky. But her best friend had stormed off the field and kicked a folding chair into the air.

Tiana had looked up at her friend, standing, fuming, and said, "If you had enough energy to kick a chair, you should have played harder. There's no point in having any energy now. Leave it on the field."

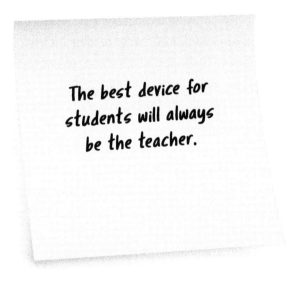

The best device for students will always be the teacher.

Tiana knew, sitting in her living room looking around her, that she was not "leaving it on the field." Some effort was there, but that wasn't good enough. Looking at Jill working so hard made her realize she wasn't working as hard as she could.

She reached for her phone, and within two rings Jill was on the other end of the line, obviously surprised to hear from her.

"Thanks for picking up," Tiana said. "I realize your generation uses text messaging to talk. When is the last time you received a phone call?"

Jill laughed. "It's nice to talk to someone on the phone once in a while."

"I love the lesson you designed," Tiana said. "I feel so lost around technology. I want you to teach me how to do some of this stuff. I need your help."

"Of course I'll help you!" Jill said. "It is really not hard once you get started."

"Is it possible to start with some basics?" Tiana asked.

"Sure," Jill replied. "When I was in college, we talked about the difference between using technology as a replacement tool as opposed to a modification tool. My professor introduced us to a model called the SAMR model, which stood for 'substitution, augmentation, modification, and redefinition.'"

"Look at you, throwing educational jargon and acronyms my way!" Tiana said, laughing.

Jill laughed too.

"The idea is, when you use technology, it shouldn't be just a worksheet on a screen. You have to think about designing tasks that make learning different and create outcomes that were previously impossible."

"I think you lost me already," Tiana responded.

"Let's sit down during our off period tomorrow and go through some things," Jill said. "I would love to help you."

Tiana felt a bit embarrassed at being so far behind the curve. On the other hand, when the students were behind in her class, she would tell them, "Just do anything. Just get started. Take one step, however simple." And now she was taking her own advice and addressing a real problem.

A quotation from Humphreys sprang into her mind. *The Road has only two rules: Start and Continue.*

"Baby steps," Tiana said, walking toward the kitchen. "Let's just start and figure out where we need to go."

Tiana's Journal

When I first started writing this journal, I thought it would be for you. Now that I've gotten to this entry, I realize that part of this is actually for me. When I was in your classroom today, I felt like teaching had passed me by. I mean that in the right way. The innovation I saw in your room was honestly amazing. Today, you connected your students to some students across the country. You redefined and modified the learning task in a way that would have been inconceivable without technology. It was cool, fun, and quite honestly, inspiring to watch.

I'm reminded of something I read by Marshall McLuhan years ago, The Medium Is the Message, and now many things he talked about are so relevant in our world.

There are now these devices, cell phones or laptops or whatever comes next, that are portable, instantaneous, and global. This has never been a possibility in the entire scope of human history, and looking at you in the classroom, I realize that this new technology needs to be implemented by younger people who can understand how to use it. But can I offer a caution? Let's not forget that the definition of a tool, the original definition of a tool, is anything that extends the human hand. So a hammer is a primitive tool because it extends the range and power of the human hand.

This new technology has so much power that we need to be careful about what it means for young people. Remember that people are, and always will be, more important than technology. They're more important than hammers, and they're more important than cell phones. The thing I loved about your lesson today was that it was centered on the kids. The global nature of technology has so much power, and it was exciting for me to watch it being used responsibly by you.

Back in my classroom, I looked at my lesson plan, and I realized I have so much to learn from you and from others in our department. I've been relying on some of the same lessons year after year. I know how tiring it is to think about backwards design, create new assessments, and keep up with technology. You have many things to learn as a first-year teacher, but you found time for this, and it was an honor to observe you.

Many veteran teachers know how to run a classroom, and they also know how kids learn. They get a free pass on lots of little things because kids just trust in them. But if a veteran teacher is willing to accept the challenge of moving forward, the rewards can be out of proportion with the time and effort we put into it. We know what is going to work in the classroom and how to do it.

Thank you for pointing the way for me. Thanks for showing me that there is this exciting element to teaching I hadn't even considered before. (Okay, that last sentence was a lie. I'd considered it before. But it frightened me so badly that I needed help. So thank you for offering to help me.)

20

The school held its parent-teacher conferences in the enormous gymnasium. Individual tables dotted the space for teachers and parents to meet. The atmosphere in the gymnasium was equal measures sporting event and county fair as the teachers and parents were about to begin the evening.

Day to day, the teachers at Silverado School dressed in their most comfortable business casual wear, but today everyone had dressed more formally. Jill, who had felt painfully underdressed for her first day of new teacher orientation, wore a conservative skirt suit. Jill was nervous, and her nerves sprang from two different reflections. The first was that she had very little to say to parents, and the second was the fear that the teachers next to her would hear some of the difficult conversations she would be forced to have.

When the clock ticked to 1:00 p.m., a member of the maintenance staff unlocked the gymnasium doors, and parents entered in a wave. First, they picked up their child's report card, and then they made their way to speak with individual teachers.

Like any business, we have customers, and it's all too easy to think that a school is there to serve itself. But our real customers are in the community we serve, and they need to believe that we're hearing their concerns and questions.

The first parent to visit Jill was the father of a diligent boy in Jill's second period class. The boy had experienced trouble, early on, grasping the more abstract concepts of the class, but he had a solid work ethic and genuinely wanted to improve.

His father was an older man with a shock of gray hair swept back from his face. He walked up to Jill's table with a sense of inherent authority. Jill stood and shook his hand.

Jill started with a general description of the class then moved on to a description of the boy's performance in class.

"Giovanni is so conscientious," Jill said. "He always does his homework, so he has a mastery of the material when we get to the quizzes. I can tell that he studies hard for quizzes and tests. He has an 82 percent for quizzes and a 79 percent for tests. Some of his group work could be better, and I think I need to be more careful about assigning Giovanni to groups that help him be more productive."

Giovanni's father nodded slowly as Jill spoke and glanced down at his son's report card, lying flat on the table. The lead of a mechanical pencil rested by the title of Jill's class.

After listening to her description, he shrugged.

"When I was in school, things were much different," he said brusquely. "I mean to say, they focused more on skills, you know, like grammar, subjects and verbs. These days the kids don't know the difference between a verb and a noun. Giovanni says he is on his computer working, but I never know what he's doing or what it has to do with schoolwork."

"Well, to be fair to Gio, most of his homework probably can be completed on the computer. Unfortunately, that could come with many distractions."

"We used to have memorization drills all the time," Giovanni's father continued, as if Jill hadn't spoken. "We used to have to memorize multiplication tables, famous poems, sections from the Bible in Sunday school." He patted the table in front of him gently with a calloused hand. "That is how young people learn," he said.

"Giovanni is a wonderful boy," Jill said. "I'm lucky to have him in class."

"Giovanni is a good boy, you're right," his father said. "But like all boys, he needs discipline. If a boy doesn't have discipline, he can't get a good job. When I was in school, the nuns used to wear us out. I can tell you they saved a lot of lives by being harsh," Giovanni's father said. "But I have taken enough of your time already. Thank you for what you do for my son."

He stood up and moved away slowly, and a few more parents met with Jill to speak about their sons and daughters. Unfortunately, many of the parents that arrived at the beginning of conferences were parents she did not *need* to see. After a few conferences that consisted almost entirely of good news, Jill began to realize that the challenge of parent-teacher conferences was bringing in the parents that she *needed* to see.

Later in the evening, Jill found herself face-to-face with a short woman with a red face, who peered intently at her. She was holding the hand of a three-year-old boy.

"I am Diana's mother," the woman said.

She shook Jill's hand nervously and sat down, pulling the little boy onto her lap. She pulled a bag of peanut M&Ms out of her purse while Jill began describing the class.

Diana's mother gave a peanut M&M to the child on her lap. Just as Jill was about to start speaking about Diana's individual progress, the child started to gag.

He tried to cough and started wheezing. Jill stared in increasing horror as the child started moving around with discomfort.

Suddenly, the woman looked down and realized what was happening. She balled up two fists together and, in one smooth motion, brought them down on the boy's abdomen. The M&M shot out of the boy's mouth and struck Jill in the forehead.

> Parents want to know if you really "know" their child. Make sure to include some personal information, and keep the conversation as positive as possible. Is it positive? Is it necessary? If the answer is yes either time, say it.

Jill did not know what to do. She sat motionless. She looked straight ahead and then blinked. The moment lasted, but the woman seemed to be waiting for her to speak.

"Diana has an 87 percent in quizzes, and it seems that she studies conscientiously," Jill said. She paused, and for a moment she did not know how to continue. She felt that she wasn't doing justice to the girl, Diana, and who she was as a person or as a student.

Diana's mother looked quizzically at Jill, and Jill glanced at the screen of her laptop nervously.

"I'm sorry, I just don't think that I'm doing a good job of describing Diana and her academic progress. She does good work in my class, but . . ." Jill's voice trailed off.

Jill tried again, and when she started to speak, her words came out in a steady flow.

"Diana is a really sharp girl. When she reads, she not only understands what she is reading, but she makes a connection to something else, maybe to something that she heard in history class, a current events topic, or maybe even a novel that she's read, but the connections are always there. The only thing I really worry about is that Diana won't have the chance to get enough experience to make the connections she's capable of making."

Jill paused, but Diana's mother was looking at her so intently that she continued.

"She's a really bright girl, and she's clearly capable of doing high-level college work. I wonder if she knows that. I haven't told her, but I know she is going to be successful at something."

Jill leaned forward, and her voice took on a passionate, ringing tone.

"I like Diana," Jill said. "She should go to a great university because she will make use of every chance, every opportunity, that anyone ever gives her."

Jill stopped speaking for a moment, and a feeling of slight embarrassment came over her.

"I'm sorry, I didn't mean to put any pressure on her future. I just wanted you to know that your daughter is a very special person."

Diana's mother broke into a giant, beaming smile.

"No one has ever spoken that way of my daughter," she said. "They always say she's a good girl. She does her work. She is polite with the other students. But you really think that she has talent?"

"I was in college just last year. So I can tell you what college students think like, act like, and write like. Diana can do college-level work someday. She just has a knack for figuring things out, and I want her to have all the opportunities she can get to make sure that she becomes the student she was meant to be."

Diana's mother thanked Jill and warmly shook her hand.

As she left, Jill reached up and felt her forehead and wiped away the small bit of moisture that clung to her skin from the peanut M&M that had been ejected from Diana's brother's mouth. She looked to her left, and she saw a colleague laughing with disbelief. He had seen the entire thing. Jill smiled and broke into laughter too.

Before she had a chance to fully process that interaction, she looked up to see Matt, a student from her first period class, and his father marching toward her.

Her stomach tightened.

Matt frequently missed class, worked lethargically when he was there, and often "forgot" to turn in assignments. The looks on the father and son's faces told the entire story: The man's face was a mask of well-concealed fury, and the boy's face was sullen and pouting, his eyes directed at Jill. Both of them glared at Jill as they approached her table.

Matt's father greeted Jill abruptly as soon as the three sat down at the table. He turned to Jill and started speaking in rapid-fire style. "I don't understand what is going wrong in your class," the man began. "My boy doesn't want to be there. I have to fight him every inch of the way to do homework for your class. He says that all you do is lecture and give them notes. Where is the teaching in that? How am I supposed to know what he has due and when? By the time the grades are entered, it's too late to do anything about it."

Jill could feel the blood rushing to her face. Her mouth became dry.

"First of all, thank you for being here tonight," Jill said calmly. "I've tried to get you on the phone a few times to talk about Matt's progress. As you can see from his grade, I'm very concerned about how he is doing."

Jill reached forward and touched her laptop screen, following a line of Matt's assignments.

"I see three—no, four—missing homework assignments, and two missing quizzes that Matt never made up. I also see a 55 percent as a grade on our first unit test. Then in unit two, there are two missing assignments, homework . . ."

Matt's father interrupted, "Can he make any of that work up?"

"The work that he's missing in this unit can be made up for partial credit," Jill said.

"What's the sense in that?" Matt's father asked. "Isn't the whole point to make the kids learn? Shouldn't he get full credit for any work he does this semester?" He was almost shouting.

"I'm following school policy, here," Jill said. "Student work done within the unit is accepted late for partial credit."

"So tell me, Ms. Cordera, is there a chance he is going to pass this semester?"

Jill said, "Honestly, it would probably take a Christmas miracle for that to happen."

Matt's father sprang from the folding chair, shoving it back several inches. "I'd like to speak to a member of the administration," he said loudly.

Standing, Jill frantically looked around for a member of the administrative team. Her eye caught the attention of one of the deans, and she waved him over. Assessing the situation at a glance, the dean strode quickly toward them then guided Matt and his father to a private office at the corner of the gym. Jill sat down and tried to calm herself with a few deep breaths. She felt bad that an administrator had been forced to control a situation she should have been able to contain. Jill looked over at Tiana, who, although she was in the middle of a parent conference, met her eyes and nodded to her encouragingly. Jill rubbed her temples as she waited for the next parent to sit down.

In the auditorium, Brian greeted parents as they walked in for the administrative presentation. He had volunteered to do a question and answer session that would resemble a town hall meeting. The idea was to allow parents to ask questions of the vice principal and talk with one another for a half hour.

Brian had been a teacher at the school for six years before moving into administration. He understood the school and how it functioned, and he felt pretty confident that he could answer any of the questions that might come up. He expected someone to mention the increased drug use by the students.

While he was prepared for that part of the town hall meeting, he was not prepared for the onslaught of questions he received from parents that night.

The first parent started off the evening confrontationally. "What is the school doing about the fighting between gangs in the hallways?"

"We don't have a gang problem," said Brian. "When I first got here as a teacher, I felt like we were breaking up a fight every week. Now, we probably have a fight every month or so. The school has really made a lot of progress in making sure there is no longer a gang presence."

Brian's tone was defensive, but he believed what he was saying. Referrals for fighting and gang activity were very low compared to previous years. He wondered how he could change the perception of the parents and the community. The biggest problem that administration had run into in the past was messaging. He stared out into the auditorium and wondered what he sounded like to the group of parents in front of him.

The questions continued.

"Why weren't parents notified about the lockdown drill until twenty minutes after it ended? My daughter was texting me about it before the school said anything," an angry woman in the back of the auditorium said.

Before Brian had a chance to reply, another parent stood up, a heavy-set man in a ball cap. He waved his arms until Brian nodded in his direction.

"What is the school doing about transgender students wanting to use the bathrooms of the opposite gender?"

His question rang through the auditorium, and before Brian could answer it, another parent in the second row on the side called out, "We've heard from our daughter that she is being bullied. What are you doing to stop it?"

Brian stood still, taking in the scene, which had spun out of control. He felt the need to start answering the questions, rather than just giving the parents a chance to complain, but the moment for that seemed to have passed. He stood in front of the parents listening to their concerns and trying to remember them all so that he could address them. He could feel his hands growing clammy.

Most of the questions were fair. The topics were meaningful to the parents and deserved to be addressed. Some of the questions were overly specific, relating to either one student or a very small group and would have been better spoken about in a one-on-one session. It seemed like all of the questions related to controversial topics.

As he stood in front of the parents, turning from one angry comment to the next, he wondered if there were right answers to any of these questions and if the parents were even asking questions at all.

Many of the parents seemed caught up in an eagerness to vent about what the school was doing wrong, and Brian felt powerless to stop the assault. It was an odd dynamic that seemed to be compelling parents to bring up the most inflammatory comments.

He offered some answers. The bathroom issue for transgender students was an ongoing issue that the school was doing its best to address with fairness and sensitivity. Bullying was a rare event in the school, but when it occurred, the deans handled it well.

As he stammered through his answers, the room became increasingly restless with more and more comments from the crowd.

He held on through a drawn-out discussion of how the teachers' salary schedule was tabulated. Really, he just stood there watching the debate that raged between one parent who said that the teachers were earning too much and another parent, an earnest woman in a scarf, who wanted the rest of the parents to know how hard it was to teach kids these days.

As Brian's hand got clammier, he became afraid that he would drop the microphone to the floor with a thud of defeat.

"Thank you all for coming tonight," Brian said, in what he hoped was a convincing tone after the session ended.

"Your questions were really good, and I hope you trust that I answered them as fairly as I could. In the instances when we're talking about an ongoing process, I promise that the school will keep you informed as best we can. We appreciate all of you being here to support your sons and daughters."

— 21 —

Jill walked into Taft's behind Tiana, and the sounds of the crowd hit her like a wall. The laughter and loud voices flowed from groups of teachers with some administrators scattered among them. Jill joined Tiana at the bar, and Tiana bought her a beer. They turned around and surveyed the crowd.

"It's good to see everyone out," Tiana said. "There aren't many chances for us to get together, but when it happens, I realize how much I need it."

The young teacher with black glasses walked up to Jill and said hello as Tiana moved to speak to some friends.

"I heard you had a little trouble with a parent," he said.

"Yeah, just a bit," Jill said. "I think they handled it."

She took a sip of beer then looked out across the room. The memory of the angry parent was mellowed by the friendly voices and laughter around her.

"Did any of the administration talk to you about it?"

"What's to talk about?" Jill asked. "I screwed up and lost control of the situation. Where's the conversation in that?"

The man in the black glasses took a half-step back and looked at Jill appraisingly. "Do you think they're going to?" he asked.

"Hard to say." Jill shrugged and moved away from him.

She saw the colleague who had seen her get pelted by the peanut M&M. Even the sight of her made the man laugh. "Jill, the way you handled that? You are unflappable! You just kept on talking after that M&M hit you."

Jill laughed and rubbed the invisible M&M mark on her forehead. "Just a candy-covered surprise," she said.

Moving through the room, she passed another group of teachers. Jill overheard the woman with blonde frizzy hair saying, "I just am counting down the days until the season is over."

Jill glimpsed Brian, standing across the room. He saw her and smiled. He moved out of the group of older teachers, and they met in a clearing in the crowded bar.

"How did that parent meeting go?" Jill asked.

Brian shook his head and then smiled ruefully.

"They were pretty tough on me," he said.

"How so?" Jill said. "What were they saying?"

"It was like a list of all of the most controversial topics you could imagine," Brian said.

"How did you do?" Jill asked.

"I'd call it a qualified disaster," he said.

"How qualified?" Jill asked.

"I'd only qualify it by saying that I tried my best, and at no point was I physically harmed."

"So that's a win," Jill said. "How did you get it to end?"

"I asked if there were any more questions. It's a conversation killer." He shook his head at the memory then asked, "How was your night?"

"A parent started yelling at me, and one of the deans had to bail me out."

Brian nodded reflectively, and they both took a sip of beer.

"Well, that'll happen to the best of us," he said.

"It won't. I mean, it doesn't," Jill said. "But thank you for saying that."

Someone called Brian's name, and he nodded to Jill and joined a group of administrators who stood nearby.

Jill looked across the bar, and suddenly it felt inviting and comfortable, a community separate and apart from the school. Even being in physical proximity to those she'd only passed briefly in the hallway felt like a strange acceptance, as if she had become a member of a club.

She watched a group of older men who were laughing about a story one of them was telling.

"That happened thirteen years ago! You can't remember what day it is. How do you remember this stuff?" one of the men said.

"I'll never forget the look on his face," continued another man.

"No, and this is the truth, the referee told me I couldn't say that word while I was on the field. And I can't repeat what I told him after that."

"And you were surprised when he threw you out?" one asked.

Jill smiled at the conversation between friends who had worked together for years.

Jill looked at an older man sitting casually alone watching the television screen above the bar. She followed his eyes to the screen and watched a few seconds of what was obviously a poorly produced action movie. A man jumped from a helicopter onto a moving railroad car. As he completed his jump, the man at the bar started laughing, which made Jill laugh as well.

The man turned his attention from the screen to Jill. "It's all so stupid," the man said chuckling. "I mean, the physics alone . . ." But the man was unable to continue as he let out another loud laugh. Once he regained his composure, he introduced himself to Jill.

"I mean, there's nothing wrong with stupid entertainment, but *really.*" The man paused and shrugged. "I'm glad I'm a teacher," he said unexpectedly.

"So you don't have to jump out of helicopters?" Jill asked.

The man laughed again.

"People wait their whole lives to be a hero, to step up and change a life. Teachers get that chance, that opportunity, every single day. You know, in the movies they tell you these stories about people in this one moment of action. The truth is that teaching kids, education, is a game of inches. Every day. One small win and getting pushed back. And then a few inches forward. And that's your teaching career."

Someone called to him then, and he turned away from Jill after a quick nod. Then Tiana was at Jill's elbow asking her if she was ready to go. Jill glanced across the bar once more, struck by the reality that so much had happened in all of these people's lives during this school year so far. Their days were filled with meaning, minute-by-minute, packed with interactions that had consequences. Some days, it seemed when she tried to remember something that happened earlier in the day, the moment seemed so far removed it might as well have been a week earlier rather than a few hours. Then looking at this room full of teachers and administrators, she thought how all of those moments they had experienced in the course of the year multiplied into an almost incomprehensible number—one that added up to the life of this building, this school.

Tiana's Journal

What a night. At the end of the day, when things get difficult, when we have a rough contract negotiation, another district initiative, a difficult class, a losing season, or like tonight, some crazy situations . . . at least we have each other. Tonight proved that this profession is all about people and the relationships we carry with us.

That said, what happened today deserves some examination. Parent-teacher conferences can be one of the most rewarding days of the school year, and they also can include some of the most difficult conversations.

Jill, I hope you read this journal entry now and then again in ten years when your life has changed, and it has changed you. You will read it differently, and I hope that you'll understand the difference.

When I was a young teacher, I liked talking to parents and appreciated all the wonderful conversations we had. I loved when parents would nod their heads as I spoke about their kids because I noticed some of the same things about their sons and daughters that they were noticing at home. Other parents would take my side as I talked about the struggles with their child. They knew exactly what I was talking about. Some parents enabled their kids, and you could see it from a mile away. Other parents weren't the nicest or the most trusting. Parent-teacher conference day was usually a positive experience because the conversations all centered on a shared passion between the parents and myself. Their kids. Our kids.

But if one thing is true, it is that the way I spoke to parents changed the moment I had children. When I went to parent-teacher conferences for the first time for my son, I hung on every word the teacher said. I could not wait to hear what the teacher said about him, figure out if she really "knew" him, and decipher whether or not she cared about my son's trajectory. I dissected every word. I analyzed everything and talked to my son about it afterward. It was like the Super Bowl of being a mom. Every mom wants to feel like Tom Brady in that moment. I know we spoke about some of your tougher moments tonight. When you say, "It would take a Christmas miracle to pass," to a parent, well, I can see how there might be a negative reaction. I know you didn't mean it as an insult, and I know that student probably has no chance of passing, but word choice is important. You are not the only one who has chosen words too quickly without the benefit of reflection. We make the best choices we can in real time because that's the time that's offered to us.

Brian had some difficult conversations and questions that came from parents. There is opportunity for growth here, too. Brian makes a lot of mistakes, but he has the right disposition. In order to grow, you have to walk into rooms that are too big for you. If you are the smartest person in the room, you have probably outgrown it. If everyone in your world looks to you for answers, you have to find yourself a more challenging environment.

Part of our responsibility in education is to get out of our small rooms, where we may feel important or relied on, and enter into spaces, conversations, and challenges that force us to grow. This isn't a license to be underprepared, but it is a call to test our own limits. It is okay to be vulnerable and honest talking to parents. Parents are our single greatest partner in working with our kids.

When you talk to parents as a teacher, the parents will listen closely. If you have kids, you will listen and internalize just as much. Never forget that you are working with and caring for the parents' only irreplaceable asset: a unique and wonderful child who is hopefully cared for and loved unconditionally in the home. While our love for our students may come close, it will never be as strong as a parent's love for his or her child. Speak to each parent knowing that your words have an enormous impact.

22

Silverado School's professional development took place on a few days each school year. When Jill asked Tiana about it, she said, "It's a chance for teachers across the district to work on curriculum together, revise common assessments, and sometimes we listen to educational experts." After a pause, she said, "Almost everyone in the district knows that most teachers would rather spend the day with students rather than being herded into an auditorium and talked at all day, but for some reason we keep doing it."

The morning session focused on helping teachers access data about common assessments.

In the afternoon, Jill and Tiana joined their department to work on the upcoming units in their professional learning communities, or PLCs. The number of strong personalities in the room made for some interesting theatre during the PLC time.

"Our students cannot read this excerpt," said Steve, one of the veteran teachers in the room, pointing at a section on the common unit exam with a sharp jab of his finger. "I gave this test last year, and I got dozens of questions about the prompt, let alone the passage. If our kids can't even read the question, how are they supposed to answer it?"

"My students did just fine with it," responded Dave, a younger teacher, with a shrug. "I don't see the problem with challenging them on this and maybe grading a little more leniently."

"That seems hypocritical," said Steve, throwing himself back in his chair. "I thought we were supposed to be norming up the way we assess our students. Remember? Stick to the rubric?"

As Dave and Steve's voices grew louder, Jill thought about their concerns. Both had a logical point of view, but it seemed that their personal beliefs had overtaken the purpose of the collaboration.

Jill sat quietly and listened. Tiana had told her that one way to navigate a department effectively was to be very strategic about speaking at meetings. She tried to take her cues from Tiana, who had seen many of these professional disagreements take place over her career.

"All I am saying is that we are doing a disservice to our students if we are giving them questions they cannot read and readings that they cannot comprehend," the veteran teacher said. "I am all for challenging our students, but this question is just pointless."

Jill looked at Tiana, who was now ready to move into the conversation.

"Leveling down the text, questions, and vocabulary won't help any of our students either," said Tiana. "We have to continue to challenge the kids and provide support along the way."

Jill listened with intent to what Tiana said. Their conversation reminded her of what Brian had said about text complexity in her formal evaluation.

"What are you trying to say, Tiana?" Steve said. "I provide my students support, and they still struggle to read."

"It's not like that, Steve. I am just in favor of challenging students when we can. I would rather have them wrestle with higher level material than breeze through something easy."

"Totally agree," Dave said. "And we can still give students a break when we grade it so that we acknowledge the progress they are making."

The room fell silent for a moment. Clearly there were two different "camps" forming in the room, and much discussion would ensue at the end of the meeting. The department chair was attending a leadership meeting, which meant that no one was there to referee, and the battle would continue another day.

Jill and Tiana walked out of the room together after the larger group discussed a few more questions on the unit exam.

"Steve seems pretty angry about that test we just gave, huh?" Jill observed.

"It's hard, Jill," said Tiana. "We want to challenge our students, but we also don't want to demoralize them with frustrating tasks. I think Steve is coming from the right place, and Dave is too."

Always remember...
curriculum: we
teach kids.

"Isn't the district pushing us to present challenging texts to students? The research backs up what you were saying."

"Do you think Steve cares about the research?"

"I don't know," Jill said.

"Steve sees what is in front of him," Tiana said. "He knows our students really well, and he thinks he understands what is best for them. We all think that way."

Jill paused. She didn't think that way. She was too busy just figuring herself out as a teacher.

"The important thing is that we can leave the room having had a respectful dialogue. Curriculum is not a life-or-death situation. It is not an emergency. We can be passionate and articulate but still be professional."

"When should I start to speak up at these PLC meetings?" Jill asked. "I feel like I don't have a place at them, but I want to contribute when I can."

"Your approach has been really good so far," Tiana said, approvingly. "Some teachers will hold it against you if you walk into these meetings and act like you have all the answers when you're in your first few years of teaching."

As they turned the corner to their hallway, Tiana turned to Jill. "Let me tell you a story really quickly," she began. "When I was in my first year, a veteran teacher arrived late on a Friday. A herd of students stood outside his room after the bell rang, and I hung out in the hallway just to supervise them. When he walked in five minutes late, I pretended to look at my watch and asked him, 'You just getting here?' I was totally joking because I thought we had a good relationship up to that point in the year. He looked at me sternly and said, 'Who's askin'?' I thought it was weird. Later that day, I found out he was really upset with what I said to him. He told everyone in the department what had happened, and a bunch of my colleagues were mad at my comment."

"But you were joking," Jill said, defensively.

"I *was* joking, but he didn't interpret it that way," Tiana said. "You never know how people will interpret what you say. Some teachers will talk behind your back when you ask them for their lesson plans or an answer key. Some teachers want you to struggle through your first year because they struggled through their first year. Some teachers don't want you to work harder than they do because it makes them look bad."

Jill thought for a moment. *Are teachers around me upset that I borrow worksheets and lesson plans from them? Do they talk about me behind my back?*

This first year, she didn't really even have time to think about all those things.

"Tiana, I really haven't been aware of those types of things," Jill admitted. "I have been struggling just to stay two pages in front of the kids."

Tiana laughed.

"No one expects you to lead these curriculum teams yet or even to share your materials with others. You'll find your place. During the first year, people just want to see your work ethic and your personality."

"Work ethic and personality?" Jill asked.

"Work ethic and personality," Tiana repeated. "That's it."

Tiana's Journal

We often get caught up in our own philosophies and beliefs on what should be taught, how it should be taught, and how we should assess student progress. As much as we want curriculum to be unified and consistent, the methods we use to teach it will always vary from teacher to teacher and will always be very important to the students' growth.

Teacher autonomy is vital in our profession. There is a reason why there aren't cameras in classrooms. There is a reason students prefer certain classes over others. It's the ability to put our own spin on our content and skills that makes our profession unique. We have to honor and respect the fact that each teacher creates a different path for his or her students to reach the finish line.

Inevitably, some teachers will clash over curriculum and judge one another based on those discussions about what and how we teach. We cannot let our own egos overtake the power of our collective work. When you have time, look at John Hattie's research on shared teacher efficacy and how it drives student achievement. Simply put, we are better when we work together.

As a first-year teacher, you have to pick your battles. The truth is, most teachers do not contribute to PLC work for a few years because they are still building their own methods of preparation and delivery. But remember, your colleagues are always watching. If you are doing creative and impactful things in class, others will see it and admire it.

23

The students and the faculty at Silverado were moving through the year, but to Brian, the end was not yet in sight. His days were full as he scheduled proctors, articulated test procedures, and organized accommodations for students. State testing was quickly approaching. Added to that pressure was the need to focus on staffing for the following school year.

Principal Pasztor and his administrative team had some hard decisions to make during the next few weeks, and many of them wanted to have one last look at the new teachers. Brian had begun to make his final rounds to informally evaluate all of the untenured teachers and report back to Pasztor. Once summative evaluations were complete and the board approved a budget for the following school year, the administration would finalize staffing for the next year.

As Brian approached Jill's room to take one last look at her teaching, he thought about how Jill's first observation had gone. She had grown significantly through the year, and he hoped that by entering her room one final time, he would see something inspiring and be able to make note of it. At the very least, he was pretty sure he'd watch a well-planned lesson.

Brian thought he had won the relationship with Jill, and he thought she had done the same with her students. It would be nice to put this one in the win column and move on.

Brian quietly opened the door and saw all of the students on their computers. With ten minutes of the class remaining, it appeared the students were beginning their homework assignment.

The class was silent and, if nothing else, on task.

Jill was seated at her desk in the corner of the room. Brian looked at her, and he was suddenly aware of how much she had been through in the course of the year. She looked tired, and her eyes had a strange focus to them. She was looking down near her computer, though it did not appear that she was looking directly at it. When Jill glanced up and saw Brian, she jumped quickly out of her chair. As she did so, she knocked her cell phone off the keyboard onto the desk with a clatter.

Brian winced. She had been on her cell phone while the students were working on their homework. The school had a strict no-cell-phone policy for students because there was a mountain of research that the distractions were detrimental to student learning. While there were no formal directives for teachers, it looked bad when they used their phones in class.

Jill moved quickly out into the room and started walking down one of the aisles, looking at the students' computers as she went.

"I am noticing that some of you are missing question five," Jill said to the class as she moved through the aisles. "If you think about yesterday's lesson and the simulation we did, it should help you arrive at the right answer."

A few students shuffled through their notes, and one student even said, "Got it!"

Jill stopped at another student's desk and looked at his screen. He glanced up at her over his shoulder and said, "This reading is really hard. I don't know what some of these words mean. Like, this word right here," he said pointing to the screen. "I've never seen the word 'ambiguous' before."

Brian sat down in an empty student desk, thinking about two different things. He was watching the students work, but he was also thinking about Jill, sitting at her desk, on her phone.

Part of him wanted to dismiss the event. She had been on her phone, but on the other hand, few, if any, of the students had actually seen her. For a teacher who had experienced some problems in the classroom throughout the year, the thought that she hadn't taken her good fortune and his leniency in the evaluation process seriously made him furious.

Folks who act with integrity have nothing to fear. They almost always do the right thing.

The class was in really good order, however, and there seemed to be a clear sense of direction to the lesson. One student was talking text complexity, and that had come up in Jill's observation.

She was clearly addressing things they had talked about. Her reaction to their conversation made him feel that he could trust her to react positively to feedback.

He went back and forth, thinking about what he'd seen.

How often does she sit at her desk? he wondered. *Why couldn't she wait ten more minutes for class to end to send a text?*

"As I am walking around, I like a lot of what I see," Jill said. "A reminder to everyone that tomorrow is Friday. So if you finish this assignment, your homework is to make sure you bring in a clean, non-ethnic, non-racial, and not necessarily funny joke to share with the entire class."

"Why did the man put his money in a freezer, Ms. Cordera?" a student shouted from the second row.

"This one again, Jeremy?" another student groaned.

"Because he wanted cold, hard cash," Jeremy answered. He laughed, and the joke was met with an even mixture of laughs and groans.

"All right, all right," she said, smiling. "Save your best material for tomorrow when we begin class."

Brian had heard about the Friday ritual in Jill's class earlier in the year, but he had never seen it. The last time he asked her about it, she said that one of her teachers in high school used to have "Joke Friday," and each class would begin with a few students volunteering their best clean humor for the class. She had explained it as a way to engage the students in something fun at the end of the week, and she was hopeful it might motivate the students to work a little harder in the remaining forty minutes of Friday's class.

Brian loved it.

He valued classroom culture over everything else. He always thought that students learned better when they were having fun, and he had read research to back up this commonplace assumption.

When he was a student teacher, his cooperating teacher held to a teaching philosophy as brief as it was effective: "Work the kids hard and have fun with them."

In his years in the classroom, he had grown to believe in the power of that philosophy. Bell ringers and opening activities established routines to begin the class, and research could prove the advantages of using the first few minutes to extend assessment of student learning or to preview coming attractions of the day's lesson.

Brian had always been a fan of a good mixture of fun and productivity, and he loved that Jill chose to carry on a tradition in her class.

When he was a first-year teacher, he had admired how one of the older teachers, Nick, had run one of the most productive and fun classes he had ever seen. He had finally gotten up the courage to ask Nick for some teaching pointers.

The older man had looked at Brian over his reading glasses and traded Brian a question for a question.

"Can you tell a joke? Are you funny?" Nick asked.

Brian shrugged. "I mean, I'm not hilarious or anything, but, yeah, I can tell a joke."

"Get 'em laughing. It helps the medicine go down," Nick said.

It was the only teaching tip Nick offered, but it had been a good one.

As Brian was thinking back to his colleague's advice, the bell rang. Jill scurried out of the room with her computer to cafeteria duty, and Brian walked slowly through the hallways, which were suddenly crowded with students.

Brian was deep in thought, and it was a matter of some concern to him that he wasn't walking with his eyes on the students, greeting the ones he knew and saying a simple hello to those he didn't.

When he got back to his office, Brian sat motionless at his desk, wondering if he should address Jill's phone use in the classroom.

"Win the relationship," played over and over in his head.

Jill had been on her phone.

How could he mention that *and* mention the strong culture in her room?

He thought about the conversations he had with Tiana during the year and remembered that when he took this administrative job, his number-one priority was to make sure the students received the very best opportunities to succeed from their teachers and the school. He'd found himself teetering between micromanaging and always finding the good in people. It was not a good feeling, and he questioned if he would ever resolve this tension.

Brian opened up his computer and typed an email to Jill.

Hi Jill,

Thank you for letting me hang out in your classroom today. It was nice to see all of the students on task, and it certainly seemed like they understood what you were asking them to do. I really liked that one of your students was struggling with the vocab in the text set you picked for them. My schedule is insane tomorrow, but I would have LOVED to stop in to hear Jeremy's encore for Joke Friday tomorrow. Classroom culture always wins!

If I don't see you before then, have a good weekend!

Brian

PS: What did the custodian say when he jumped out of the closet?

"Supplies!!!!"

Brian read the email back to himself, then he sent it. He stood up from his desk then turned and looked out the window.

Am I doing the right thing? he thought.

After teaching her last class, Jill opened up her computer to find Brian's email at the top of her inbox. The subject line read, "Informal Evaluation today," which scared her a bit. Jill replayed the scene in her mind of Brian walking in, and she cringed. She had been texting.

Jill knew what she had done was excusable because it related to a family concern. Her father had been feeling dizzy lately, and twice now he had actually lost consciousness. He had gone to see a neurologist about his fainting spells. Her father had just texted Jill to give her the welcome news that the test results had come back, and he was perfectly fine.

Although Jill had been seated when Brian walked in, she always walked around the room when the students worked individually or in groups. It was rare for her to sit down.

Jill remained a little nervous to hear if Brian would comment on "Joke Friday."

She read the email, and it surprised her. She reread it and then smiled. Brian hadn't offered her any substantial feedback, but as she reread the email, she realized how badly she needed his positive comments. Either Brian hadn't seen her texting, or he wasn't concerned about what he had seen. Either way, she forwarded the email to Tiana.

She knew she shouldn't forward emails from an administrator, but she wanted Tiana to know about the good news.

24

The next day, Brian and Tiana pulled into the nearly empty parking lot at almost the same time. Tiana noted that Jill's little blue hatchback, usually already parked underneath a tree near the edge of the lot, was not there. She parked next to Brian and greeted him as they walked toward the school with their workout bags over their shoulders.

"Back on the workout schedule in the morning, huh Brian?" said Tiana.

"I couldn't sleep again last night and woke up at 4:00 a.m.," Brian groaned. "I figure, if I cannot fall back asleep, I might as well come into school and work out a little bit."

"Let's hope there are a few ellipticals left for us," she responded. "Hey, I saw you walk into Jill's room the other day. Did everything go all right?"

"For the most part, it was good. I was not in there long. I don't spend as much time in the rooms unless I have a concern," he said and smiled.

"I think she is feeling a lot more comfortable now and starting to settle in," Tiana said. "I'm really proud of her."

"I am too," Brian agreed. "I am proud of many of our new teachers in the building this year. We really have a great group. I just hope we can keep them all for next year. Staffing meetings happen next week, so we'll know more then."

"Good luck with those meetings," Tiana said. She entered the women's locker room to get ready for her workout. After forty minutes on the elliptical, she quickly showered and ran up to her classroom. Feeling frazzled, she beat the kids to her door by less than ten minutes. She saw Jill at the same time. A group of students waited for the doors to be unlocked.

"Morning, Jill," Tiana said. "Is everything okay? You're always here way before seven."

"I was up late grading papers," Jill responded. "I set my alarm for this morning but hit snooze a couple times because I was absolutely exhausted."

Tiana nodded, and she smiled kindly at Jill.

"I figured you went out partying after Brian's observation." Tiana lowered her voice. "I got your email. I'm glad it went well. It has to be a relief to you."

"Absolutely," said Jill. "Between my dad's health, all these papers to grade, planning my classes, I just feel like I haven't caught my breath at all recently. I can't sleep more than five hours, and I am still really nervous about getting rehired next year."

The bell rang, announcing that first period would begin in five minutes, and students started to pour into both Jill and Tiana's classrooms.

"Sounds like you need more time for yourself," said Tiana.

"There is just never enough time. A few days ago, I saw that you were here working out early in the morning, and I miss that. When I get busy, one of the first things I have to cut is working out, and I need that to feel good about my day. When I lose the things I like doing, it just makes all the other things that much more stressful."

> Thought leader James Clear says that your life is like a four-burner stove. Imagine that every burner represents a major responsibility, like career, family, a serious hobby or interest. You will always have to turn off one burner to devote the proper time to the major issues in your life. You can really only focus on three major areas at one time.

Tiana nodded. She thought back to when she had been a new teacher. She remembered living on her own for the first time, handling the stress of the job, and balancing family, social, and school commitments.

"You're doing a good job balancing all of this, Jill. I remember going through learning how to teach, and somehow I made it through to the other side. Let's talk about balance again when we've got more time."

"I appreciate your support," Jill responded. "Honestly, I've got this. I just need to worry about today." Jill paused. "Well, I sort of need to worry about tomorrow too. My summative appointment is at 1:45. I'll find out if they offer me a contract tomorrow."

The second bell brought the conversation to an end. Balance would have to wait.

Stress is temporary. Understand the value of time and spend it doing things that fill your soul.

Tiana's Journal

It is clear to me that you have made some great strides as a teacher, Jill. I am excited for your path and your willingness to improve. I know that you have improved so much in the past few months, and I'm so very proud of you. Regardless of what happens with your contract tomorrow, you are a teacher, and you will be for some time.

Let's talk about self-care. I know you are under a tremendous amount of stress, but I think our concerns are only compounded when we don't take care of ourselves. You are responsible for 150 students every day. How do you expect to take care of them if you are not taking care of yourself first?

I remember Brian telling me this story about a conversation he had with a staff member. The staff member asked him, "If you are going to be putting this new initiative on my plate, what are you going to be taking off?" As you and I know, Brian is the type of person who adds more than he subtracts, so it doesn't surprise me that he responded by saying, "I haven't thought about what we should subtract first."

Obviously, the staff member did not take that well.

We all reach a limit where our plates are full. Sometimes we do this to ourselves, and other times our lives create the situation for us. Regardless of the circumstances, it's important to prioritize the things we must accomplish, and include several things we want to accomplish too. I know that working out, hanging out with friends, spending time with your family, and reading are all important to you. So as you work to put those things back on your plate, could you grade papers more efficiently through peer review? Could you go home a little earlier a few times a week?

Nothing is more important than caring for ourselves because we have to be well in order to care for others. We can make other things a priority for a while, but we have to go back to this truth eventually. Always remember that there are people who would love to have your bad days.

25

Across the school district, the last Friday of April was known as "Black Friday." First year teachers, from kindergarten through high school, knew this was the day they would find out whether they would receive a contract for the upcoming school year.

Jill's assessment meeting was at 1:45, and the time on her computer screen told her she had just a few minutes more to wait.

"We have a few minutes left. Does anybody have any questions?" she asked the class. No one raised their hand as she moved around the room. She remembered too late that the question was a conversation killer. She had asked the question out of habit, but listening to the silence, she knew class was over for the day.

"No questions?" she asked again. "In that case, you can have the last few minutes to yourselves, and we can pick it up again tomorrow."

Jill returned to her desk, looked at her email, and then at the time: 1:36.

She felt a small lump in her throat.

"Oh, and I almost forgot," she said, "We'll have a quiz on Monday over what we covered this week."

"We know, Ms. Cordera," said a boy sitting near her desk. "We have a quiz every Monday."

"I just wanted to make sure everyone remembered. Maybe you can take a look at your notes in these last few minutes and make sure you're ready," she said with a smile.

The boy smiled too. There were only three minutes left in the period, and he knew that Ms. Cordera's suggestion was as serious as his studying would be, but Jill was too distracted about her meeting to argue.

He turned around and began talking with his friends as Jill returned to her desk and looked back at the computer screen.

1:39.

Her palms began to perspire. In just a few minutes, she would know whether she had a job for next year. Jill thought about her experience this first year, and somehow, she was relieved that she'd find out soon whether she had a job to come back to in the fall.

She closed her computer and grabbed a notepad and a pen. There wouldn't be many notes to write down from the meeting, but it was best to look prepared.

1:40.

The bell rang, and the students began to file out of the classroom. She took a deep breath and held it then exhaled slowly. She nodded to herself, turned out the lights, closed the door, and walked out into the hallway.

Looking down toward the windows to the courtyard, her mind went back to the first time she had walked down this hallway to her own classroom. She'd felt like she had needed to pinch herself to make sure that it was real. She actually had a job teaching something that she loved! And then the reality of teaching had flooded in. On the walk to the principal's office, she wondered if it would all end here on this day.

When her phone rang on an April morning almost a year ago, the Assistant Superintendent offered her a job at Silverado. He was friendly, but he spoke in a clipped, professional manner.

Jill remembered saying, "I would love to teach at Silverado." Then, suddenly she was holding her phone, and there was no one to talk to because he had hung up.

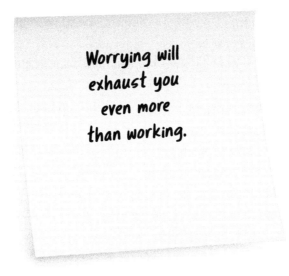

Worrying will exhaust you even more than working.

Jill looked around the kitchen and thought, *Just like that. I'm a teacher.*

Moments from the school year came back to her. Jill's first day flashed into her mind, and she remembered her nervousness and inability to relate to the students. She thought of Camilla. Their relationship had come a long way from its rocky start. She remembered her first evaluation and how she had reacted to it, but mostly she thought of all of the students' faces, crowding into her classroom, sitting down to experience something together, in one community. She even thought about all of the advice she had received, and a vision of Professor Strus's post it notes on her refrigerator came into her mind. She was within a dozen feet of the principal's office now, and she realized that all of those moments had defined her growth as a teacher, but this moment would be as important as any.

The principal's secretary greeted Jill with a smile and asked her to take a seat until Principal Pasztor was ready to see her. With her nerves alive, Jill treated everything she observed as a sign.

The secretary smiled at her.

Does that mean I'm getting a contract for next year? Jill thought.

The door was closed.

Is administration in there thinking of a way to give me bad news? Jill wondered.

Jill felt the gravity of this moment, the moment that would alter her career. She'd heard a rumor about "Black Friday" that it was better to have an appointment early in the day. Her appointment was at the beginning of the "bad news" period. The gossip was that administration always wanted to push out good news first, so they scheduled all of the meetings for teachers who would be rehired early in the day. Jill knew the decision to hire her for the following year would not have been an easy one.

Suddenly, the door to the office opened, and Principal Pasztor stood looking at Jill. "Come on in," he said. "Let's get started and get right to it here."

Jill stood and walked into the office on unstable legs. The principal gestured to a chair in front of his desk for Jill then sat behind his desk. He pushed a button on his desk and the door swung closed behind Jill with an ominous click. Principal Pasztor seemed distracted by the large amount of loose papers on his desk. Jill watched him shuffle through them as he began to speak.

"I'm sorry, Jill. We do not have a contract for you at this time. That official paperwork is still being finalized as the board and union work out the collective bargaining extension. We do have a provisional document that guarantees you a position on staff next year. Congratulations! We cannot wait to have you back at Silverado!"

Jill exhaled and smiled.

"Whew, you scared me with how you phrased that," said Jill, breathing heavily. "I was already worried after getting the late appointment that—"

"Not to worry Jill," Pasztor said, cutting her off. "We think the world of you. Don't worry about the appointment time. It was just a scheduling issue. We think the best is yet to come for you as a teacher, and we hope you sign this agreement to join us again next year."

"Of course. Where do I sign?"

Pasztor placed a thick sheaf of papers on the desk in front of her and gave her a pen, which trembled slightly in her hand.

When gratitude is high, entitlement is low. When entitlement is high, gratitude is low.

"Right there," he said, tapping on the document with his finger. Jill signed.

It was official. She had made it through her first year and had been offered a job for the following school year.

"Thank you, Mr. Pasztor. I just cannot thank you enough for every opportunity I have been given this year," she said. "Is that it?"

"That is all, Jill. I have another teacher coming in right after you. Are you planning on going out after graduation with all of us?"

"I wouldn't miss it," Jill said, beaming, and she walked out of the office.

26

Jill woke up to the alarm at 5:25 a.m. on graduation day. For Jill and the rest of her colleagues, it was going to be a long day, and Jill had decided to make it even longer by getting up early to make time to exercise. With the encouragement of several of her colleagues, she had begun a routine of working out in the morning at least twice a week again. Today she planned a three-mile run on one of the school's treadmills. She jumped out of bed, excited about experiencing her first graduation at Silverado School.

There was still a long day of classes ahead, and Jill had a solid lesson plan today. Her classes would be debating in their teams, and she would be working with student judges to score each team's arguments. It felt good to have a great lesson plan for the day, and she was reminded of the beginning of the year when she had been scrambling to get through one period. After working out, Jill ran up to her classroom with enough time to set up her room.

"Ladies and gentlemen, we now have our winners!" Jill's voice echoed down the hallway. "Is that not a sweet win right there for the Hawks? You guys dominated that debate!"

> What you work on,
> works on you.

The class erupted into applause. The other team yelled encouragement as they watched the winners hold the championship belt proudly.

Tiana walked back from the mail room and noticed the excitement in Jill's room. She peeked in to find Jill wearing a referee jersey and holding a whistle looped around her neck. She had a penalty flag in her back pocket and a stopwatch in her hand.

Jill continued. "All right. Let's switch the teams out. The teams that just debated are now becoming our new judges. Great job by the Hawks, winning their first debate of the year."

Jill ran a lesson plan she called "debate sports" where teams were divided into four different groups. Each pair of teams was responsible for one side of a controversial question.

The homework the night before had been to research their side of the argument and present it to the class in a logical and convincing way. The half of the class not debating acted as judges standing on the sidelines. Jill served as referee.

"I cannot believe you guys lost that," a member of the Hawks team said to an opponent across the aisle. "Cordera totally set you up with the easiest side of the argument."

Jill heard the comment and moved close to the boy who was speaking.

"If it was so easy, they would have won," the other boy said.

Jill smiled at the student on the losing team. "You did a nice job."

> The best things we do often stem from small changes made with great conviction.

As the next two teams quickly took their places to get ready for the opening argument, the previous teams opened up their tablets and quickly answered the reflection question Jill had preloaded in a form. The reflections acted as a check on whether the students understood the purpose of the debate. Jill collected all the answers on a spreadsheet that was sortable by student. This way, she could track the growth in their writing and reflective responses throughout the year.

Jill had not been watching the time, and the class period passed so quickly that the bell rang before the second debate could begin.

"Hold on, everyone," Jill shouted as the class began to move their desks back into place. "I am sorry we didn't finish today. We'll pick up there tomorrow and don't forget—"

"Yeah, yeah, we know," a student interrupted. "Reflection forms are due by midnight whether or not you debated today or not."

"That's exactly right," said Jill, "but that is only half of what I was going to say . . ."

"Cordera! Cordera!" shouted a student. "Why did the picture on the wall go to jail?"

"Yes, tomorrow is Joke Friday! Extra credit for any student who remembers to bring in a clean, non-ethnic—"

"Non-racial and *not* necessarily funny joke tomorrow," said the first student, finishing Jill's sentence.

Tiana stood at the door, watching the students file out, and thinking back to the beginning of the year when this scene of genuine excitement would have been unthinkable coming from Jill's classroom.

"It was framed," said Tiana to Jill as she walked into the room.

"Pardon me?" responded Jill.

"The joke. Why did the picture go to jail? Because it was framed." Jill chuckled.

"You heard that, huh?"

"Priceless!"

"Debate sports tend to get a little crazy, but I think the kids have fun with it," Jill said.

"I was standing out in the hallway to watch the fun," Tiana said. "I'd love to steal this activity, but honestly, I don't think I could recreate the culture you've made. What do the reflections look like? Do they usually do a good job on those?"

"For the most part," Jill said. "There are still a few of them who don't always turn it in. I am still dogging some of those kids for their missing homework."

"I saw that Allen was engaged," Tiana added. "He was probably the weakest student on the winning team, and the other kids were treating him like he made the difference. I couldn't get Allen to pay attention to anything we did last year."

"It was weird; one day I overheard him talking about Puerto Rico's four, four, two formation in the World Cup game. I jumped in. He was off task as usual. I told him I thought they should have gone four, three, three to strengthen their back line. After that, he started to turn a few things in, and we talk soccer almost every day."

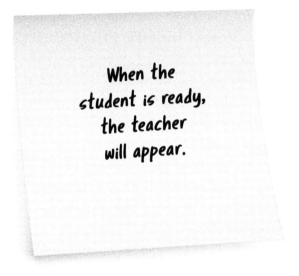

When the
student is ready,
the teacher
will appear.

"I'm proud of you, Jill," Tiana said. "What a fun lesson."

Jill smiled and nodded.

"Are you ready for graduation?" Tiana asked.

"I think so," Jill said. "Let me grab my cap and gown."

Tiana and Jill rode together to the small hall where the graduation was to take place. On the way they traded small talk, knowing their conversation couldn't match the importance of the moment.

As she walked into the hall with Tiana, Jill saw the students whom she had taught scattered in small groups of parents, students, and other faculty members. She was struck by the hushed conversations emphasizing the seriousness and accomplishment of the moment.

Jill saw the boy with reflective sunglasses from her class. She walked toward him, unsure how to greet him now that he was no longer her student.

"Ms. Cordera," he said. "I'd like you to meet my parents. Mom, Dad, this is Ms. Cordera, my favorite teacher."

Jill shook their hands warmly.

"We've heard a lot about you," the boy's father said. "Thank you for making this guy interested in school again. He talks about your class all the time."

"I don't know what you do in class," his mother said. "But he always does your homework first, and I can't remember the last time he asked me to look over an assignment before he handed it in. He always has me check his work for your class."

The boy shook his head. "You're embarrassing me," he said.

"It's true," his father remarked, ignoring his son's comment. "He even had me read some of his best work aloud. He's never had me do that before."

Jill smiled. "Well, congratulations on your son's achievement. It's just such a happy day. I'll see you in there," she said, nodding to the doors of the auditorium.

Next she saw Camilla, standing alone in the middle of the foyer. She began walking toward the girl, who immediately broke into a smile when she noticed Jill. In a sudden rush of emotion, Camilla ran toward Jill and threw her arms around her in a hug.

"Thank you so much for everything you've done for me," Camilla said, still holding Jill. "My parents couldn't make it today, but I feel like you are a part of my family, so you're it."

Jill's eyes welled with tears. "Camilla," she said, taking the girl's hands, "I would be honored to be one of your family."

"You really made me do my best in class. Seeing you there every day made me want to try really hard. Thank you."

"Camilla, I've enjoyed having you as my student *so* very much."

You can be rich
without the
dollar signs.

"Okay, I'm going to go and get ready now," Camilla said. She stood for a moment, just looking at Jill. "You know, at the beginning of the year, I didn't think that I was going to learn so much from you. Thanks for working so hard to change my mind."

"I'm really glad you were in my class, Camilla," Jill said.

The girl gave her another quick hug before moving toward the auditorium.

Jill looked around the foyer at the students who were caught halfway between their families and their school life. Jill had not known what graduation would be like; she was excited but apprehensive. Her nerves were still raw with too little sleep and too much worry. But on some level, she realized that the year was really over.

Is this what the entire year was about? Jill thought. *Sending these students out into the world?*

Jill reflected quietly on the importance of graduation, but just then the lights dimmed twice to signal that the ceremony was about to begin. Jill stood still, watching families, friends, students, and colleagues slowly make their way toward the auditorium doors.

She saw Tiana, threading her way toward her.

"Are you ready to do this?" Tiana asked as she approached Jill.

"I don't know if I'm ready for this year to be over," Jill said.

"Well, there is one thing we have to do before we walk in there," said Tiana, nodding at the auditorium doors. She reached into her bag and brought out a plainly bound blue composition journal. She looked at it for a moment then handed it to Jill.

"It has been one of the most profound pleasures of my career to watch you grow. I've enjoyed it more than I can tell you. Throughout the year, when there was something that I thought you should know, I would write about it. For you and also, I suppose, for me. Sometimes I was able to tell you about it, and sometimes I wasn't. But I wanted to give you something that you would always have to remind you of your first year."

Jill's hands trembled as she held the book. With tears filling her eyes, she opened it to the first page, which simply read: "For Jill. I hope these lifelines keep you afloat, Tiana."

She hugged Tiana, and both women smiled and laughed a little as they dabbed their eyes.

"Thank you so very much for everything you've done for me," Jill said.

"And thank you for everything you've done for *me*," Tiana replied.

Side by side, they moved toward the auditorium doors.

Tiana and Jill heard their names, and they turned as Brian approached them.

"Didn't think you were going to make it," Tiana said to Brian.

"Did you mean 'make it to the graduation ceremony' or 'make it to the end of the year'?" Brian asked.

"Now that you put it like that, a bit of both," Tiana said. "You know what the funny thing is?" she asked.

"No. What?" Jill asked.

"We get to do this all over again next year," Tiana said, and the three of them turned and walked toward the auditorium doors.

Jill looked at Brian and Tiana.

"I honestly can't think of anything I'd rather do," she said.

ADVICE FROM THE AUTHORS

Many of the stories and experiences that happened to our main characters were modeled after things we've experienced in our own careers or in our work in other schools. We wanted to give you a short checklist of things to think about as your school year progresses. So here it is—a list of our top tips for maintaining a smooth functioning classroom, working well with others, as well as reminders of other important duties, and advice on how to make teaching your career.

Classroom Advice

1. Chronicle everything. Keep handwritten or typed summaries of every class period. You will refer to this when planning next year, and it will save you a lot of time.

2. Run your lesson plans by your mentor teacher. Especially if you are being observed, it always helps to have an extra set of eyes on your lesson plan before you execute.

3. Grade papers at school. If you use time in planning periods, before and after school, and maybe even while students are testing, for the most part, you can avoid taking

work home. This is one part of achieving a good work/home life balance.

4. Call parents when you are concerned. Talk to the students first and give that relationship a chance to grow. When it doesn't seem like the student is catching on, call home and begin working on establishing that relationship too.

5. Call parents to share the positive things. There is nothing better as a parent than hearing positive things about your child. Every parent wants to have these moments. Grades only communicate part of the story of student progress. Talk to parents about things other than objective academic measures.

6. Our job is to teach the students. All of them. Every day. Some students can go a full day without hearing their names called. Engage with every student in some way, every day. This will help the relationships you build individually and collectively with the class.

7. Begin each lesson with a purpose. Some younger teachers really need to start with a bell-ringer and something to focus the students' attention. Veteran teachers can use this time to engage with their students or to entertain them. Both strategies work. But where is the lesson going? Students have to know the "why."

8. Always over-plan. The feeling of ending a lesson with ten minutes to go and having to tap dance in front of the kids to fill time is the worst. Over-plan activities and opportunities for students and be satisfied knowing you maximized their learning time.

9. Use your body as much as your voice. Proximity is a teacher's best friend. Raising and lowering your voice will rarely have an effect on attention or behavior. Move around

the room, stand near students who need extra attention, and look at their computer screens often. Look at Pavel Goldstein's work. Kids love it when we sit in student desks to join their group work, kneel down to speak to students at their level, and when we give high-fives.

10. Be the guide on the side, not the sage on the stage. This is the trendiest advice in teaching, but it is true. Why are we the ones who are always exhausted at the end of a long day of teaching? The students should be the ones who are tired from thinking, talking, writing, and analyzing.

Working with Others

1. Make friends with every support staff person you can. These positions are essential in the school and are often filled by the most real people you will find. Thank and value every bus driver, food services, maintenance, fiscal services, and support staff member. They work to make your job easier. Never forget it.

2. Be cool with sharing space. Some teachers can be territorial about their space. You've never had one before and pretend like you never will. Most teachers now share classrooms and are lucky to have their "own room."

3. Ask people about themselves. Try to look at every social conversation as 80/20. Try to listen and ask questions 80 percent of the time and take 20 percent of the time to respond to questions or talk about yourself. Most people love talking about themselves. Folks will see you as an easy person to get along with if you give them the opportunity to speak. (Some people may take even more of their 80 percent.)

4. Play "dumb" with gossip. If someone asks you, "Did you hear about so and so?" just politely respond with a "no," even if you may have heard some gossip. Don't ask any follow-up questions or leading comments that allow for more conversation. With each story or opportunity for gossip, ask yourself, "How does knowing gossip about this person make me any better?" Another litmus test for your comments: "Is it positive? Is it necessary?" If the answer is no both times, best not to say it.

5. Get to know your principal. You will probably not see or hear from your principal other than in large assemblies, emails, and the public address system. Value the moments you can converse one-on-one and make sure you get to know him or her beyond what you see externally.

6. Birthdays and funerals are important. No matter what people say, almost everyone is excited on their birthday. A simple card or acknowledgment goes a long way. As difficult as it may be in your own schedule, do everything you can to attend the funerals or wakes of a colleague's family member. There is great power in presence.

7. Keep great company among the staff. Try to seek out the teachers who are the most well-liked and well-respected among the staff. You will be able to tell right away if a teacher fits this category. If the district assigns you a mentor, show deference and willingness to learn from them. Our veteran teachers have so much to share with us.

8. Make or bring in food for the department every now and then. Food brings people together. Bring in something homemade or something sweet for everyone. It goes a long way in making people happy.

9. Positive impressions often start with preparedness. Whether you are planning a lesson, contributing to a PLC, or running a practice, one of the first ways to earn a good reputation is being prepared. Almost all of us have struggled to execute all of these things perfectly. That is okay. But if you fail to plan, you are planning to fail. Most colleagues you work with will value your preparedness.

10. Keep all interactions with adults professional when in front of students. One of the most damaging things we can do in front of our students is engage in conversations that are unprofessional in nature.

The Intangibles of Teaching

1. Show up early. Staying late can mean a lot of things, but when people arrive to work early, usually they are working. Folks will notice. Beyond that, it's usually quiet early in the morning and you can accomplish a lot.

2. Dress professionally. People will rarely talk behind your back if you are overdressed, but they sure will if you are underdressed. Treat teaching like a professional endeavor.

3. Attend extracurricular events. Students love seeing us at their sporting events, plays, musical performances, dance and cheer competitions, etc. The best sides of our students often reveal themselves in these spaces.

4. Try to attend social events with the staff. These are the moments that make teaching fun. Very few other professions release at 2:30 or 3:00 p.m. Enjoy the extra time in the afternoon once in a while and socialize with your colleagues. You do not have to stay late, but be present.

5. Show a willingness to do things without being paid. In union-minded staffs, teachers like to get paid for everything

they do outside of their contractual obligations. None of us went into this for the money. No teacher is paid what they deserve, honestly. But because we are not in this for the money, can we be present for kids because it is the right thing to do and not something we necessarily get paid for?

6. Take attendance. It may seem like something small, but attendance is a legal document. Take attendance within ten minutes of each period and try to be as accurate as possible. In potentially serious situations, it's important to know where the kids are.

7. Pick your places to contribute within your learning community. Keep your eyes open and your mouth shut? Well, not quite. Try to listen to understand rather than listen to reply. Understand your role as a new member of any department and pick your spots to contribute. Find opportunities to lead by example, not necessarily by being outspoken.

8. Engage with other teachers on social media. There are so many opportunities to learn with other teachers in person and online. Attending conferences takes time away from your students and your family, and potentially can be costly. Some of the newest, best models of professional development are completely free. Try social media like Twitter or join Facebook groups for your discipline and age group.

9. Enroll in a master's program right away. There is never a good time for graduate school. You will find that it only becomes more difficult as your career continues. Most teacher salary schedules will reward you for an advanced degree. If you have a chance to learn more and get paid more for doing so, what are you waiting for?.

10. Try to visit and observe other schools. Sometimes you can do this through professional development or by studying other programs that schools are using effectively. It helps

build a teacher's perspective to see other teachers working in different conditions with different students. This is especially true if you have worked at the same district your entire career.

Making Teaching Your Career

1. Save the good, bad, and impactful. Every card, note, letter, or moment that moves you to tears? Save it in a folder. When you hit a rough patch, go back to that folder and read a collection of all of these moments throughout your career.

2. You always have each other. There are moments in your career where you feel isolated. Whether you are supervising, coaching, or teaching, there are other adults around you. Value each other and know that these can be some of the most impactful and lasting friendships in your life.

3. Be honest with yourself in applying for other jobs. Thinking about becoming an administrator or supervisor? Do you really want to leave the classroom? If so, great. But do you know in your heart of hearts you are doing so for the right reasons? You can rarely go back, so make sure you are reflective in this decision.

4. Plan the best vacations you can. Teachers have the summer off! Well, a lot of them do. If you can find any time to get away, take advantage of flight and hotel prices midweek since you are off in the summer. We don't earn a lot of off time during the school year, so take advantage of it during breaks.

5. When dealing with disappointment, the lights will be shining very brightly. Whenever people know you are going through something difficult, everyone will be watching to

see how you respond. If you don't get the schedule you prefer, have a bad evaluation, or get passed over for a job promotion, folks will be waiting to see how you respond. Be at your toughest and most professional in these moments. If you aren't, you will give other people all the ammunition they need to understand why you didn't get that schedule, earn a good evaluation, or score that job promotion.

6. Be incredibly cautious with social media. Who you are online is who people think you are as a person. Try to set a good example for your students by only posting and interacting online professionally. Everything can turn into a screen shot or something controversial. Before posting something, ask yourself, "Is it worth it?" or "Would my grandmother approve of this?"

7. Maintain friendships outside of education. Most of us will have no problem with this one. However, sometimes we realize how lucky we are to work in this profession when we hear stories from friends who work outside education. It's also important to understand that other jobs and careers have challenges, stresses, and in many cases, tremendous pressure too.

8. Take time to reinvent yourself. One of the easiest ways to burn out is doing the same thing you have always done. Especially in subjects like science and math, the numbers and the theories don't really change. But we can change. We have the ability to teach and deliver differently. Take time to explore new and exciting ways to make your content and skills relevant to your students and to you.

9. Be human. This is a job. But this is a job with enormous impact. You have signed up for a career in human relations. The importance of being accessible and working well with others cannot be overstated. Never take yourself

too seriously, unless you are attempting to understand the power you have to change the trajectories of thousands of students. Those who can . . . teach. Never underestimate the power of what you are doing every day.

10. Find your lifelines.

For *Finding Lifelines* book study questions and other resources for professional development, scan the QR code or visit **andrewsharos.com/bookresources**.

WITH GRATITUDE

Some authors retreat to a secluded cabin in the woods to write a masterpiece that can only be made possible by controlling their outside environment. We wrote this book in between the craziness of family life, full-time jobs, graduate school, and publishing our first book. Hopefully that proves that writing impactful stories isn't always about controlling the outside environment but more about sharing what is inside of us with the world.

Of course, the ability to do that could have never been possible without our extraordinary support systems.

To Dave, Shelley, and the entire DBC Pirate family, we are incredibly grateful for your belief in this project and the unending support we have received along the way. Landing in your publishing family was an absolute gift.

To Dr. Harry K. Wong, who generously wrote the foreword to our book, thank you for believing that this fictional story does come to life in classrooms everywhere, every day. Your feedback on mentoring, coaching, and tutoring helped frame our main character's life.

To Leyden High School District 212, thank you for assigning us study hall supervision duty together over a decade ago. Our conversations began there. Your support of our work and how it impacts teachers and students around the country is appreciated.

To our co-workers, friends, and family, we could not have done this without you. Whether it was feedback on an idea, a helpful ear that listened, or the encouragement and inspiration to keep writing, your presence alone has pushed this book across the finish line.

To our collective children, David Grieve, Ana Grieve, Cooper Sharos, Parker Sharos, and Beckett Sharos, we love you more than anything.

Finally, to fellow educators everywhere, thank you for everything you do for your students. We survive and thrive in the greatest profession because of the connections we share with our kids and connections we share with one another.

MORE FROM
DAVE BURGESS
Consulting, Inc.

Since 2012, DBCI has been publishing books that inspire and equip educators to be their best. For more information on our DBCI titles or to purchase bulk orders for your school, district, or book study, visit **DaveBurgessconsulting.com/DBCIbooks**.

More from the *Like a PIRATE*™ Series

Teach Like a PIRATE by Dave Burgess

eXPlore Like a Pirate by Michael Matera

Learn Like a Pirate by Paul Solarz

Play Like a Pirate by Quinn Rollins

Run Like a Pirate by Adam Welcome

Lead Like a PIRATE™ Series

Lead Like a PIRATE by Shelley Burgess and Beth Houf

Balance Like a Pirate by Jessica Cabeen, Jessica Johnson, and Sarah Johnson

Lead beyond Your Title by Nili Bartley

Lead with Culture by Jay Billy

Lead with Literacy by Mandy Ellis

Leadership & School Culture

Culturize by Jimmy Casas

Escaping the School Leader's Dunk Tank by Rebecca Coda and Rick Jetter

From Teacher to Leader by Starr Sackstein

The Innovator's Mindset by George Couros

Kids Deserve It! by Todd Nesloney and Adam Welcome

Let Them Speak by Rebecca Coda and Rick Jetter

The Limitless School by Abe Hege and Adam Dovico

The Pepper Effect by Sean Gaillard

The Principled Principal by Jeffrey Zoul and
 Anthony McConnell

Relentless by Hamish Brewer

The Secret Solution by Todd Whitaker, Sam Miller, and
 Ryan Donlan

Start. Right. Now. by Todd Whitaker, Jeffrey Zoul, and
 Jimmy Casas

Stop. Right. Now. by Jimmy Casas and Jeffrey Zoul

They Call Me "Mr. De" by Frank DeAngelis

Unmapped Potential by Julie Hasson and Missy Lennard

Word Shift by Joy Kirr

Your School Rocks by Ryan McLane and Eric Lowe

Technology & Tools

50 Things You Can Do with Google Classroom by Alice Keeler
 and Libbi Miller

50 Things to Go Further with Google Classroom by Alice Keeler
 and Libbi Miller

140 Twitter Tips for Educators by Brad Currie, Billy Krakower,
 and Scott Rocco

Block Breaker by Brian Aspinall

Code Breaker by Brian Aspinall

Google Apps for Littles by Christine Pinto and Alice Keeler

Master the Media by Julie Smith

Shake Up Learning by Kasey Bell

Social LEADia by Jennifer Casa-Todd

Teaching Math with Google Apps by Alice Keeler and
Diana Herrington

Teachingland by Amanda Fox and Mary Ellen Weeks

Teaching Methods & Materials

All 4s and 5s by Andrew Sharos

Boredom Busters by Katie Powell

The Classroom Chef by John Stevens and Matt Vaudrey

Ditch That Homework by Matt Miller and Alice Keeler

Ditch That Textbook by Matt Miller

Don't Ditch That Tech by Matt Miller, Nate Ridgway, and
Angelia Ridgway

EDrenaline Rush by John Meehan

Educated by Design by Michael Cohen, The Tech Rabbi

The EduProtocol Field Guide by Marlena Hebern and
Jon Corippo

The EduProtocol Field Guide: Book 2 by Marlena Hebern and
Jon Corippo

Instant Relevance by Denis Sheeran

LAUNCH by John Spencer and A.J. Juliani

Make Learning MAGICAL by Tisha Richmond

Pure Genius by Don Wettrick

The Revolution by Darren Ellwein and Derek McCoy

Shift This! by Joy Kirr

Spark Learning by Ramsey Musallam

Sparks in the Dark by Travis Crowder and Todd Nesloney

Table Talk Math by John Stevens

The Wild Card by Hope and Wade King

The Writing on the Classroom Wall by Steve Wyborney

Inspiration, Professional Growth & Personal Development

Be REAL by Tara Martin

Be the One for Kids by Ryan Sheehy

Creatively Productive by Lisa Johnson

The EduNinja Mindset by Jennifer Burdis

Empower Our Girls by Lynmara Colón and Adam Welcome

The Four O'Clock Faculty by Rich Czyz

How Much Water Do We Have? by Pete and Kris Nunweiler

P Is for Pirate by Dave and Shelley Burgess

A Passion for Kindness by Tamara Letter

The Path to Serendipity by Allyson Apsey

Sanctuaries by Dan Tricarico

Shattering the Perfect Teacher Myth by Aaron Hogan

Stories from Webb by Todd Nesloney

Talk to Me by Kim Bearden

Teach Me, Teacher by Jacob Chastain

TeamMakers by Laura Robb and Evan Robb

Through the Lens of Serendipity by Allyson Apsey

The Zen Teacher by Dan Tricarico

Children's Books

Beyond Us by Aaron Polansky

Cannonball In by Tara Martin

Dolphins in Trees by Aaron Polansky

I Want to Be a Lot by Ashley Savage

The Princes of Serendip by Allyson Apsey

Zom-Be a Design Thinker by Amanda Fox

ABOUT THE AUTHORS

ANDREW JOHN GRIEVE has taught high school students for more than twenty years. He provides professional development focused on building program culture and writing/reading skills, as well as speaking at conferences. Andrew has worked as an educational consultant for the Village Project Consulting Group  for the past four years. He recently published a handbook in conjunction with the Bureau of Education and Research. Originally from the small town of Danville, Illinois, he now lives in Chicago. He has a degree in Latin and Ancient Greek, and his interests include typewriters and jazz.

ANDREW SHAROS has spent his entire career as a high school educator in Chicago.

He has been a teacher, coach, and building administrator. His students set statewide records for achievement on advanced placement tests in 2013 and 2014. He tells this story as the author of *All 4s and 5s*, an Amazon best-selling book in the AP community for classroom practices and program building. Andrew is the founder and CEO of the Village Project Consulting Group, which has provided professional development and new teacher mentoring to school districts throughout the country. His keynote speeches and professional development offerings focus on building cultures of high expectations and best practices in the classroom.

In 2014, he was a finalist for National History Teacher of the Year. In 2018, Andrew was named the winner of College Board's "Distinguished Service Award," given to a forceful spokesperson for important educational and societal goals.

Andrew is the moderator of #APTeach, a national Twitter chat focused on bringing the AP community together. The chat runs at 8:00 p.m. CST on the first Wednesday of each month.

Andrew lives in Chicago with his wife, Lizzie, and their three boys, Cooper, Parker, and Beckett.

CPSIA information can be obtained
at www.ICGtesting.com
Printed in the USA
BVHW091136060522
636033BV00006B/15